Forestry Commission Bulletin 80

G000161244

Farm Woodland Planning

Edited by H. Insley
Development Division,
Forestry Commission

Prepared in co-operation with:
The Ministry of Agriculture, Fisheries and Food
The Department of Agriculture and Fisheries for Scotland
The Department of Agriculture for Northern Ireland
The Welsh Office Agriculture Department

LONDON: HER MAJESTY'S STATIONERY OFFICE

ISBN 0 11 710266 0
ODC 26: 913: (410)

Keywords: Farm woodlands, Forestry

Enquiries relating to this publication should be
addressed to the Technical Publications Officer,
Forestry Commission, Forest Research Station,
Alice Holt Lodge, Wrecclesham, Farnham,
Surrey GU10 4LH

Acknowledgements

This Bulletin has been produced by an interdepartmental working group consisting of members of the Forestry Commission and all four Agriculture Departments as follows:

Forestry Commission
H. Insley
H.L. Davies

Department of Agriculture and Fisheries for Scotland
D.R.J. Craven

Department of Agriculture, Northern Ireland (Forest Service)
R.F. MacKenzie
G.B. Jones

ADAS (Welsh Office, Agriculture Department)
B.A. Marshall

ADAS (Ministry of Agriculture, Fisheries and Food)
R.P. Keevil

The information presented within this Bulletin has been derived from many sources. The principal contributors outwith the immediate working group (Forestry Commission unless stated otherwise) were: D.A. Bardy, S. Bell, A.J.A. Betts, R.J. Broadhurst, W.P. Carr (Inland Revenue), A. Crisp (ADAS), W.M. Dawson (Northern Ireland Horticultural and Plant Breeding Station, Loughgall), J.G. Durward, G.R. Hatfield, D.C. Jardine, P.B. Lane, I.H.L. McCall (Game Conservancy Ltd), P. Marsden (Countryside Commission), W.E.S. Mutch (University of Edinburgh), R.Q. Oakes, D. Patch, G.F. Peterken (Nature Conservancy Council), R. Prior (Richard Prior Ltd, Deer Consultants), T.J.D. Rollinson, R.M. Smith, R.D. Toleman, G.R. Watt (Economic Forestry Group plc), A. Whiteman, J. Williams

Foreword

To many farmers trees have until now often been a source of obstruction to large farm machinery such as combine harvesters and silage machines, and their only advantage was as a source of logs for the farmhouse. The arrival of serious problems with the production of agricultural surpluses has put trees and farm woodlands into a new context. With financial support from the Woodland Grant Scheme and the Farm Woodland Scheme, trees can now provide farmers with an opportunity to put their expertise as land managers and crop producers to a new use.

One of the most important requirements which they will have, given a willingness to start this new enterprise, will be sound professional advice. They will be able to get some of this from ADAS or from the Scottish College advisors or from the Forestry Commission or Northern Ireland Forest Service private woodlands staff. However, for those farmers who want to study the implications and possibilities in what for many will be a new kind of husbandry, this Bulletin and its companion volume *Farm woodland practice* provide many of the answers. Written by experts in each of the subjects covered, *Farm woodland planning* provides farmers with the kind of information needed to make the right business decisions about farm woods. I am sure that farmers – and particularly those involved in advising them – will find it a valuable reference to keep by them and that it will help them to make the most of a new opportunity in British agriculture and forestry.

Sir David Montgomery
Chairman,
Forestry Commission
May 1988

Contents

Section 1
Introduction

Section 1   Introduction

1.1 The Importance of Farm Woodlands

Woodlands are an important component of an attractive countryside. Provided they are properly planned, the planting of new trees and woodlands can benefit the countryside, improve the habitats for wildlife, and enable home-grown timber stocks to be increased.

With so many crops in surplus, timber stands out as the major exception. Only about 12 per cent of the UK market for timber and wood products is met from our own forests and this contribution from domestic sources is unlikely to rise beyond 20–25 per cent by the turn of the century.

By planting more trees on agricultural land, farmers can help to reduce the current overproduction of agricultural products while at the same time bringing greater diversity to our countryside.

Existing woodlands have often been an unmanaged part of the assets of farms and as a result contain poor quality timber. This has led many farmers to believe that their woodlands do not have the potential to produce quality timber. However, farm woodlands are often on very good lowland soils compared with those occupied by traditional forestry, and the opportunity exists in the management and development of farm woods for farmers to grow valuable high quality timber. At the same time farm woods give the farmer the chance to diversify his business, improve the appearance and often the capital value of his farm. By providing shelter and timber small farm woods may benefit the existing farm business and also contribute greatly to the farm's conservation and sporting value.

This Bulletin is intended to provide farmers and farm advisers who are planning to enter farm woodland planting and management with the management information required to plan and budget the operation. It seeks to achieve this by providing the facts farmers need to gear up their businesses in terms of planning, financial and operational aspects of woodland management, tailored to suit their individual circumstances. Figure 1.1 is a quick guide to the information contained in this Bulletin. Every effort has been made to identify the wide range of sites likely to be found on farms in England, Wales, Scotland and Northern Ireland. Each brings its own special requirements and costs for successful establishment and management techniques which will influence the value of thinnings and final crop. It is not the intention of this publication to provide practical detail on silvicultural practice and the reader requiring this is directed to Forestry Commission Handbook 3 *Farm woodland practice*.

The base year for all prices given is the financial year 1987/88. Adjustments for inflation must be made when using the figures in later years.

1.2 The Farm Woodland Scheme

In February 1987 the Minister of Agriculture announced proposals for a Farm Woodland Scheme to be introduced in 1988 for an initial period of 3 years. In broad terms the aims of the Scheme are to divert land from agricultural production, to create environmental and recreational benefits, to contribute to supporting farm incomes and rural employment, and to encourage greater interest in timber production from farms.

The Scheme will offer farmers annual payments over a number of years to help bridge the gap between the planting of trees and the likely first income from the thinning of timber. These annual payments will be additional to, and dependent on, the planting grants operated by the Forestry Commission (or the Department of Agriculture for Northern Ireland, Forest Service). The current planting grant scheme is the Woodland Grant Scheme, under which grants are available both for broadleaves and conifers but at much higher rates for broadleaves and mixtures in which broadleaves predominate.

The details of the Farm Woodland Scheme (see Section 10 for full details) have been the subject of consultation and the aim will be to plant up to 36 000 hectares (89 000 acres) during the first 3 years, mainly on improved land. The Scheme will be reviewed after 3 years to examine its success in meeting its objectives.

Other options for woodland planting on farms are also covered in this Bulletin but will not be eligible for the Farm Woodland Scheme. Some of them are eligible for other grants as indicated in the text, but others such as agroforestry and short rotation coppice are simply alternatives which interested farmers may wish to consider. The Government is, however, funding research on these types of planting.

Figure 1.1

Farm woodland planning – Sources of key information

1. Planning a farm wood

Page

Soil type and species choice	17–19
Woodland type	
Broadleaved	9
Mixed	10
Conifer	10
Coppice – traditional	10–11
– short rotation	13
Wide spaced systems	11–12
Christmas trees	13
Estimating yield	63–67
Operations required	23–27
Designing for landscaping and conservation	57–58
Grant schemes and consultation	89–92, 94–98
Taxation	92–93
Sources of advice	117–118

Identifying the cash flows

Returns from woodland investment

Section 2
Woodland Crop Systems

Section 2   Woodland Crop Systems

There are a number of ways in which trees may be grown on farms, such as conventional woodland (high forest), coppice, widely spaced tree systems, short rotation coppice or even Christmas trees and this section describes these systems in more detail. Woodland will normally be planted with the intention of growing either high value timber for sale or timber which can usefully be used on the farm or in a diversified farm enterprise. Farmers will also want to consider the important implications for landscape and conservation which are offered by farm woodlands and Section 6 together with the appropriate parts of *Farm woodland practice* are strongly recommended for reading prior to establishing small farm woods under the Scheme. This section sets out the main systems for growing trees, recognising that not all planting will be done under the Farm Woodland Scheme.

2.1 Conventional Woodland (High Forest)

This type of woodland, described by foresters as high forest, is the system in which trees are grown from seed to maturity without being coppiced, although coppice can be converted to high forest by singling. Woods of this type are usually developed by planting young nursery produced trees although they can also be developed from natural regeneration already present on the site. Before planting, the site is usually prepared by ploughing, draining or screefing (removing vegetation), and the trees are weeded and fertilised as necessary for the first few years (the establishment phase). As the trees grow the branches meet and canopy closes (thicket stage). Soon after this, the bottom branches start to die from mutual shading and thinning often begins (pole stage). Thinning (see Section 7) removes some trees, with the aim of concentrating timber volume and value production on the remaining trees. In exposed areas and on soil types prone to shallow rooting, windthrow may occur and it is usual practice not to do any thinning on these sites. This is unlikely to apply to the majority of woodland planted under the Farm Woodland Scheme which is aimed primarily at arable and improved grassland and thus better lowland soils than has been the norm for traditional forestry. The trees are finally clear felled when mature and of a suitable size for the proposed markets. Rotations are commonly 40–60 years for conifers and 80+ years for broadleaves.

Broadleaved woodland

Possible sources of grant: Woodland Grant Scheme, Farm Woodland Scheme, Set-Aside Scheme, Countryside Commission, AIS (N) (see Section 10.1).

On the types of land expected to be planted under the Farm Woodland Scheme there will be considerable scope for the planting of broadleaved woodland.

The production of a good crop of timber depends upon the competition and shading produced by close spacing to draw up broadleaves and produce tall, branch free stems of high quality timber. In small broadleaved woodlands pruning of the final crop of trees is also important if the intention is to produce high value quality timber. Pruning ensures clean knot-free timber on the most valuable part of the stem.

In the lowlands, and on freely draining soils on sheltered sites in the uplands, production of quality timber should be the primary objective for farmers. On poor quality soils and exposed sites in the uplands generally speaking broadleaved species do not grow well and are likely to produce timber of pulpwood or firewood quality only. Nevertheless broadleaved woods make a highly significant contribution to the landscape and to wildlife conservation (see Section 6).

In the British Isles the main species likely to be grown are oak, beech, sycamore, sweet chestnut, ash and the alders. Birch frequently occurs through natural regeneration but it is not often planted as a main crop species. For farmers on good lowland soils cherry and walnut provide the opportunity to produce high value timber on reasonably short (40 to 60 years) rotation.

When timber production is the primary object of management, spacings of less than 3 m are advisable. However, full grant will be paid up to 3 m spacing. Wider spacings may have benefits for conservation (see Section 6). At wider spacing than 3 m the planting grant payable under the Woodland Grant Scheme may be reduced pro rata, but Farm Woodland Scheme payments are made on an area basis and will not vary according to the density provided the planting qualifies under the appropriate forestry grant scheme. Pure oak or beech plantings (up to 10 per cent of other broadleaves are allowed within this definition) will be

9

eligible for Farm Woodland Scheme payments over 40 years and other broadleaves for 30 years.

Mixed woodland

Possible sources of grant: Woodland Grant Scheme, Farm Woodland Scheme, Set-Aside Scheme, Countryside Commission, AIS(N) (see Section 10.1).

Mixed broadleaved woodland can be more beneficial than woodland of a single species for timber production, landscape and conservation (see Section 6). The inclusion of a small proportion of a second species can give a greater structural diversity to the wood, increasing both its landscape and conservation value. The inclusion of additional species also spreads the risk of disease, damage or poor growth. The inclusion of some cherry, which is less likely to be damaged by grey squirrels, for instance in a beechwood will improve the chances of producing a top quality crop if squirrel populations are high during the vulnerable pole stage.

In general most broadleaved species can be grown together in mixtures as their rates of growth are similar. Growing mixed broadleaved woodland gives the opportunity to take advantage of the very best trees of all species to produce high quality decorative timber. When decorative timber species are being grown in mixed woodland, stems of suitable quality should be identified, marked and retained during thinning operations, and these should be pruned if necessary. The very best, defect free stems should be segregated at felling and sold separately. If the quality is high enough, buyers will come for small quantities or even individual logs.

Mixtures of broadleaves and conifers can provide better financial returns than pure broadleaved mixtures, as the conifers reach maturity before the broadleaves. If game management is important then it is often useful to have some conifers in a wood for warmth and cover (see Section 5.4). However, some broadleaved/conifer mixtures can appear unattractive in undulating country where the geometric species pattern stands out. For simplicity and robustness of design it is sensible to grow only two species in a mixture. Mixtures are usually planted in rows with three to five lines of each species alternately, or in irregular groups. In group mixtures, small groups of 12 to 25 broadleaves are planted at 10 to 12 metre centres (approximately final crop spacing) in a matrix of conifers. The alternative is to plant small irregular single species groups. It is essential to use species which are compatible (grow at similar rates) otherwise one species will dominate the other resulting in a loss of yield. Conifers are often used to help establish

broadleaves on exposed sites where side-shelter is important for early growth. It should be remembered that more than 50 per cent broadleaves must be used in order to qualify for Farm Woodland Scheme payments for 30 years.

Conifer woods

Possible sources of grant: Woodland Grant Scheme, Farm Woodland Scheme, Set-Aside Scheme (see Section 10.1).

On the types of good quality lowland sites expected to be planted under the Farm Woodland Scheme there will be opportunities to use a wider range of conifers than has been the norm in traditional forestry.

The main species likely to be grown are Corsican pine in the drier eastern half of Britain, and Norway and Sitka spruces in the wetter western half. On better quality soils in sheltered sites farmers will have the opportunity to grow other species such as Douglas fir, grand fir, noble fir, western hemlock and the larches which can produce higher volumes, better quality timber and thus a higher financial return.

Spacings are usually in the range of 2.0 to 2.5 metres because of the silvicultural requirements of the species if quality timber is to be grown. Spacings wider than 2.1 m may not be accepted within the terms of the Grant Scheme and would not therefore be eligible for Farm Woodland Scheme payments. Where wider spacing is accepted the Woodland Grant Scheme payments will be reduced pro rata but the Farm Woodland Scheme payments will be unaffected. A minimum of 5 per cent broadleaves is required in all conifer plantations except where physical conditions preclude this. In sensitive areas such as the Chilterns higher proportions of broadleaves may be required.

2.2 Coppice

Possible sources of grant: Woodland Grant Scheme, Farm Woodland Scheme, Set-Aside Scheme.

Planting to establish new coppice is eligible for grant payment, with the exception of short rotation coppice and existing coppice which is of course self-regenerating. In view of its shorter production cycle, payments under the Farm Woodland Scheme only last for 10 years.

Coppice

Coppice is the regrowth from the cut stumps of broadleaved trees (termed stools). Many broadleaves have traditionally been worked as coppice with cutting cycles of 10–30 years to produce a variety of small dimension products. Vigorous coppice species are ash, sycamore, sweet chestnut, lime, oak, alder, willow and hazel. Markets are principally pulpwood, firewood, fencing (particularly sweet chestnut) and turnery. (Hazel does not grow large enough for these products and has very restricted markets for thatching spars, bean sticks and hurdles.)

Coppice is a low input – low output system which produces a regular periodic income and needs little maintenance after initial establishment. Initial weeding and protection are the same as for broadleaved high forest. The planted maidens are then cut (stumped back) at between 5 and 12 years to induce production of a coppice stool. Alternatively the maidens can be left to grow on longer so that they yield a pulp or firewood crop when cut.

Subsequent rotations should not need weeding. The only maintenance needed is planting or layering to fill up gaps where a stool has died (usually around 5 per cent at each cut), and protection from heavy browsing in the first season after cutting. Cutting is usually done in winter.

Coppice has a high conservation value as the frequent cutting allows light in and the development of a full cover of ground vegetation. Coppice areas are also useful for low cover and flushing points for game birds (see Section 5.4).

Coppice with standards

Coppice with standards is a two-storey system, where among the coppice (underwood) some trees (standards) are grown on for larger size timber. These standards are usually maiden trees but occasionally can be coppice shoots left to grow on. The stocking of standards is usually 30 to 100 per hectare (18 to 10 m spacing) and some are harvested and some recruited at each coppice cut.

This system is useful where landscape considerations are important, as the overall appearance of the wood does not appear to change significantly even after cutting the coppice.

Stored coppice

Stored coppice is a stand of trees derived from shoots grown on past the normal coppice rotation, often with the intention of converting to high forest. The stools have been 'singled' to 1–3 stems at an early age (usually less than 20 years). Stored coppice may produce inferior timber due to increased curving at the base of the stem (butt sweep), and a higher percentage of decay and staining developing from the stools. Coppicing can be revived with most species even after a lapse of 100 years, though the percentage of failed stools increases with age. The act of recoppicing the wood provides one method of bringing woodland back into productive management, but is not eligible for grant under the Woodland Grant Scheme or Farm Woodland Scheme.

2.3 Widely Spaced Tree Systems

Most of the systems for growing widely spaced trees are not eligible for grant within the Forestry Commission or Northern Ireland Forest Service Woodland Grant Scheme or the Farm Woodland Scheme. Where wide spacing is accepted within the Woodland Grant Scheme, for example for poplar, the payments will be reduced pro rata but Farm Woodland Scheme payments which are on an area basis will be unaffected. Although grants are not usually available these and other systems such as short rotation coppice (grant may be paid on this in Northern Ireland) are mentioned here because they do present alternative opportunities for farmers.

The advantages and disadvantages of wide spacing are discussed in Section 7. The five categories of widely spaced trees discussed below are those most likely to be of interest to farmers.

Agroforestry

Possible sources of grant: not normally eligible for grant but see Section 10.1.

Agroforestry is an intimate mixture of trees and farm crops and/or animals on the same land management unit. In temperate regions it usually consists of widely spaced individual trees, groups or lines of trees in grazed or arable fields. Agroforestry systems have proved successful abroad (notably New Zealand) and are now being tested experimentally in the UK.

It is likely that in the UK grazing areas will be more suitable for this system, though poplars with arable intercrops have been grown successfully in England. The main broadleaved species suitable are sycamore, ash, cherry, walnut and poplar while the most suitable conifers are Douglas fir, Corsican pine and hybrid larch. As the trees grow timber value increases and grazing revenue declines as the grass is progressively shaded. The aim is to grow a saleable butt log of high quality timber with a minimum of 45 cm diameter (dbh) in 35–45 years, with a minimal reduction in agricultural production during the first 10–15 years.

Pruning is essential to produce quality timber, but should never remove more than 30 per cent of the live crown at one time. Careful choice of species and spacings should allow trees to reach maturity and be harvested over a long period of time (30 to 80 years) helping even cash flow and giving a more even carrying capacity for grazing stock. High rates of fertiliser to increase grass production (more than 300 kg nitrogen per hectare per year), may cause distortions to tree growth with some species, and thus reduce the value of the timber. However, for ash high rates of nitrogen are essential for good growth and high quality timber production.

Poplar

Possible sources of grant: Woodland Grant Scheme, Farm Woodland Scheme, Set-Aside Scheme.

Poplars are almost always grown in pure stands and at wide spacing. Only cultivars approved under the EC Regulations (see Section 11) are eligible for grant aid for timber production in the UK. Poplar cultivation is restricted to the lowlands, and for the black poplar hybrids, to eastern and southern England. Successful plantations are rare in N. Ireland and Scotland.

Poplars are planted at wide spacing because competition between trees is intense and the fastest growth rates are achieved by isolated trees, small groups or single rows. Spacings up to 8 m may be eligible for grant aid, although Woodland Grant Scheme payments will be reduced pro rata from the rates payable at the maximum permitted spacing for broadleaves of 3 m. Plantations are not usually thinned. Close spacings (2–4 m) can be used with *P. trichocarpa* and its hybrids, for short rotation crops producing high volumes (150–270 m^3 per ha) of pulpwood on a 12–15 year rotation. For small material (less than 30 cm) the market is usually pulpwood and for large material (more than 30 cm) veneer/packaging or coffin boards. To achieve packaging or veneer quality, pruning to 5–6 m is essential.

Cricket bat willow

Possible sources of grant: not normally eligible but see Section 10.1.

Cricket bat willow provides an opportunity for short rotation (12–18 years) high value timber production from hedgerows or riverbanks for farmers in south and east England (see Section 8). One cultivar of willow, *Salix alba* cultivar 'Coerulea', is grown specifically for the manufacture of cricket bats. Cricket bat willow can only be grown successfully in areas with a moderately warm and dry climate (not more than 900 mm per year rainfall), and on a deep permeable rich soil, preferably near to running water. Unrooted sets (long cuttings) of about 3 metres length, inserted to 0.6 m are used for planting. All branches should be pruned off up to a height of 2.4 metres at

planting and this stem should be kept free of branches by disbudding each year as necessary in the early spring. Spacing is usually 9 to 12 metres and rotation length 12 to 18 years.

Decorative timbers

Possible sources of grant: not normally eligible but see below.

Decorative timber usually refers to veneer and high quality joinery material. Exceptional stems of most broadleaved species can go to these markets, but some, notably walnut and cherry, can be open-grown specifically for decorative timber. Yew, holly, laburnum and most fruit tree timber is also used for decorative purposes by craftsmen, and this market should not be overlooked as quality material can command very high prices.

Walnut growing is restricted to central and southern Britain on well drained fertile soils in frost free areas. Pruning is essential to achieve a single main stem of 1.5 to 3 m and should be done in late summer. The aim should be to produce a final crop of vigorous trees with cylindrical straight boles at a stocking of 40 to 70 trees per hectare. Walnut is saleable at 30 cm diameter, but value increases with age. Rotations are usually 60–90 years. Both common and black walnuts produce nuts in Britain and can be grown in an orchard system for timber and nut production, though there are very few successful nut growers.

Cherry is usually grown in mixture with other broadleaved species, but can also be open grown in orchard or agroforestry systems. It should be grown on fertile, deep, well drained soils. Cherry can reach 60 cm dbh in 50–60 years. With wide spacing only one thinning is carried out at around 8 to 10 years of age and straight trees with fine horizontal branching should be retained for the final crop. For high quality stems, pruning is necessary and should be done between June and August to minimise infection by bacterial canker and silver leaf disease.

Hedgerow trees

Possible sources of grant: Countryside Commission, AIS(N) and under Scottish ESAs (see Section 10.1).

Hedgerow trees are an important source of hardwood timber. They are also of great conservation and landscape value, provide a distinct land boundary and give some shelter to livestock. Most hedgerow trees are recruited by letting existing saplings within the hedge develop into mature trees. This can be achieved by leaving small sections of hedgerow uncut for 2 to 3 years, then selecting stems of suitable species to develop into timber trees. The same thing can be achieved by planting new trees in or adjacent to an existing hedge, but expensive protection is needed if stock is present, and rabbit or deer protection may be needed even in arable country. Generally hedgerow trees should be spaced at least 8 m apart, and no thinning is necessary. The value of hedgerow trees can be improved by pruning, but generally their value will be less than a similar tree from woodland. Timber merchants disregard the bottom 1.5 m of stem in calculating volume, as this often contains metal from old fencing or rot arising from old wounds. Most broadleaved species are suitable, especially trees which do not suffer from serious disease following wounding and can also form part of a thick conventially cut hedge, e.g. beech or holly. A disadvantage of developing trees within a hedgerow is that the resultant shading tends to produce gaps in the original hedge.

2.4 Short Rotation Coppice

Possible sources of grant: Set-Aside Scheme but not eligible for Forestry Commission grants or Farm Woodland Scheme payments. In Northern Ireland a planting grant may be payable.

The concept of producing fuel wood as a short rotation coppice crop is not new but a stimulus to its development was provided in the search for alternative land using enterprises created by the serious commodity surpluses within the EEC. Work has been done in Great Britain and Northern Ireland, on a wide range of sites including good quality land, mainly through funding by the Department of Energy.

Of the broadleaves tested, poplar and willow have given the best results. In Northern Ireland *Salix aquatica gigantea* Korso (male form) has shown great promise.

The coppicing of other broadleaved species such as *Eucalyptus* and alder is being researched but information on the performance of these is limited at present.

2.5 Christmas Trees

Possible grant sources: not eligible for grant.

The growing of Christmas trees is not eligible for grant aid under the Woodland Grant Scheme or for Farm Woodland Scheme payments.

Christmas trees have often been suggested as an alternative crop for agricultural land and there has been a marked increase in planting in recent years. It is a crop, however, that is not without problems because of the cyclical nature of the market and there are growers who have lost considerable sums of money as a result. Recent calculations have shown that only a further 2700 hectares of Christmas trees will be required to achieve self-sufficiency in Britain.

In addition to the marketing risks associated with Christmas trees there are growing risks which are dependent on climate, pests and cultural techniques. Some of the latter risks can be reduced by means of a higher input regime with a consequently lower return.

The Norway spruce is the traditional Christmas tree and currently accounts for over 80 per cent of the market, but in recent years sales of pines (Scots, lodgepole and Corsican) and firs (noble and Caucasian) have increased. These species tend to have slightly longer rotations because of their slower growth.

A table of the basic operations (and cash flow) required to produce Christmas trees is presented in Appendix D, and a further table indicating the likely range of returns is given in Table 8.6.

Section 3
Soil Types and Species Choice

Section 3 Soil Types and Species Choice

3.1 Soil Types for Woodland Operations

1. Soil with well aerated subsoil

   a. Brown earths
   i. Well drained predominantly loamy soils of relatively uniform brownish soil layers. (Column 1 in Table 4.1.)
   ii. Very freely drained sands and gravels – sandy and gravelly soils. These coarse textured soils drain freely and are liable to drought in areas of low rainfall. (Column 2 in Table 4.1.)

   b. Podzols – predominately sandy and sandy loam soils with a peaty surface layer overlying a pale, bleached sandy layer above a richly coloured orange or brownish soil. Occurs in northern Britain and common on sandy heaths in the south. (Column 3 in Table 4.1.)

   c. Ironpan soils – an ironpan is a thin, hard continuous layer in the soil where iron and manganese have been deposited and which presents a barrier to root development and the downward movement of water. (Column 3 in Table 4.1.)

2. Limestone soils – these are soils with a high lime content such as soils formed directly over chalk and limestones as well as some clays.

   a. Free draining shallow soils e.g. Cotswolds. (Column 1 in Table 4.1.)

   b. Heavy soils e.g. chalky boulder clays and lias clays. (Column 4 in Table 4.1.)

3. Soils with poorly aerated subsoils including all other clay soils not covered in 2b above. (Column 4 in Table 4.1.)

   a. Mineral soils – ground water gleys with water rising from below but where draining is capable of achieving significant improvements within the rooting zone. (Column 4 in Table 4.1.)

   b. Peaty gleys (less than 50 cm peat) – these are very poorly drained waterlogged soils with an organic (peaty) surface layer, frequently occurring in areas of high rainfall. (Column 4 in Table 4.1.)

   c. Surface water gleys – heavy textured soils, wet from the surface which are improvable only with difficulty. In agricultural use major investment in drainage is required before these soils can be cultivated. These are often soils in which the water table is very close to the surface. (Column 4 in Table 4.1.)

4. Organic and peatland soils (more than 50 cm peat)

   a. Grassy, flushed or herb-rich bogs
   This group includes:
   i. *Molinia* (purple moor grass) and *Juncus* (rush) dominated bogs in areas of high rainfall. (Column 5 in Table 4.1.)
   ii. Flushed bogs – which tend to develop on gentle slopes where water moves horizontally through the soil, e.g. the flushed peats of western Scotland and Wales. These peats are often of higher nutrient status than basin bogs. (Column 5 in Table 4.1.)
   iii. Fen peats – formed in low lying areas under the influence of excessive or stagnant ground water. They may occur in areas with relatively low rainfall, e.g. East Anglian Fens, Somerset Levels and Lancashire Lowlands. Fen peats are typically rich in nutrients. (Column 6 in Table 4.1.)

   b. Unflushed basin bogs – upland, lowland and raised bogs formed under the influence of high ground water. These are very deep, soft peats usually dominated by sphagnum moss. These peats are of a very low nutrient status. (Column 5 in Table 4.1.)

   c. Blanket bogs (hill peats) – relatively firm peat, over 50 cm deep, e.g. bog peats occurring in areas of high rainfall such as Wales, the Pennines, Northern Ireland and Scotland. Typified by cotton grass and heather. (Column 5 in Table 4.1.)

Note: Many of the organic and peat soil types (Columns 5 and 6 in Table 4.1) are unlikely to be eligible for planting grants under the Farm Woodland Scheme.

3.2 Species Choice for Farm Woodlands

The choice of species for farm woodlands and the different soil types is outlined in Table 3.1.

Table 3.1 Species choice for farm woodlands

	Soil type										
	Lowland								Upland		
	Non calcareous				*Calcareous*						
	Sands and Podzols	Ironpans	Brown earths	Soft mineral soils (acid clays)	Fen peats	Free draining (shallow soils less than 30 cm to rock)	Heavy well drained alkaline clays and brown earths	Soft mineral soils alkaline gleys	Brown earths	Surface water and peaty gleys	Peat
Soil type as listed in soil types for woodland operations	1aii, 1b	1c	1ai	3a	4aiii	2a	2b	3a	1ai	3b, 3c	4
Occurrence	Lowland heaths and northern Britain	Mainly lowland heaths	Brown/red soil Mixed farming areas	Mainly clay vales	Low lying fenland	Typical soils of many chalk and limestone areas e.g. Cotswolds	Chalk and limestone regions especially of footslopes and valley bottoms	Low lying land often adjoining rivers and streams some clay vales	Upland valleys	Upland plateaus especially N. England S. Scotland N. Ireland	Upland plateau
Major broad-leaved species	Birch, Sweet chestnut, Nothofagus	Oak, Beech, Birch, Nothofagus, Sweet chestnut, Alder	Oak, Ash, Beech, Sycamore, Norway maple, Poplar, Sweet chestnut, Cherry, Alder, Italian alder, Willow, Lime, Nothofagus, Walnut, Hornbeam, Birch	Oak, Beech, Sycamore, Poplar, Sweet chestnut, Cherry, Alder, Willow, Hornbeam	Poplar, Sycamore, Cherry, Alder, Willow	Ash, Beech, Sycamore, Norway maple, Cherry, Nothofagus, Italian alder	Oak, Ash, Beech, Sycamore, Norway maple, Poplar, Cherry, Lime, Nothofagus	Oak, Ash, Beech, Sycamore, Poplar, Cherry, Alder, Willow, Lime	Oak, Ash, Beech, Sycamore, Cherry, Alder, Birch	Sycamore, Alder, Willow, Birch	Alder, Birch

Major conifer species										
Corsican pine	Corsican pine	Corsican pine	Corsican pine	Corsican pine	Corsican pine	Corsican pine	Corsican pine	Corsican pine	Lodgepole pine	Lodgepole pine
Scots pine	Scots pine	Scots pine	Douglas fir	Douglas fir	Western red	Western red cedar	Western red cedar	Scots pine	Larches	Sitka spruce
	Douglas fir	Douglas fir	Grand fir	fir	cedar	Larches		Douglas fir	Sitka spruce	
	Larches	Grand fir	Noble fir	Larches	Larches			Grand fir	Norway spruce	
		Noble fir	Sitka spruce	Norway spruce				Noble fir		
		Sitka spruce	Norway spruce					Larches		
		Larches	Western red cedar					Sitka spruce		
		Norway spruce	Lawson cypress					Norway spruce		
		Western red cedar						Western red cedar		
		Lawson cypress						Western hemlock		
		Western hemlock								

19

Section 4
Establishment and Maintenance Operations

Section 4 Establishment and Maintenance Operations

4.1 Operations Checklist

Having identified the soil type present on the site and the tree species which might be appropriate in Section 3, move on to Table 4.1, the 'operations checklist'. This helps to identify the operations which are likely to be necessary to establish and maintain a tree crop on each of the soil types identified in Section 3. Although 13 different soil types are explained in Section 3 these have been reduced to only 6 in Table 4.1. This has been done because while greater detail is needed to help identify the soil type, once identified it can be grouped with several of the others for operational purposes.

4.2 Planting Model Example for a Small Farm Wood

Once the necessary operations have been listed using Table 4.1, a planting model can be used to plan the operational expenditures required to establish and maintain a wood. Table 4.2 is an example of what one of these planting models might look like for a small farm wood and a blank proforma is provided with this Bulletin which can be copied or used to build up planting models (Appendix D, Table D.1).

As Table 4.2 shows, a planting model lists the operations required, which year they are to be carried out and the costs described on a per hectare basis. It is appropriate to quote some operations such as fencing, where the perimeter and thus the cost per unit area varies from wood to wood, on a different basis. In the case of fencing this is the cost per 100 metres of fence. This is easily converted to cost per unit area by measuring the length needed to fence the wood and then dividing the cost by the area of the wood.

4.3 Operational Costs, Quantities and Guide Times

Table 4.3 provides a description of each operation and then gives guidance on the cost and time required to carry it out. These details should be treated as indicative rather than an exact specification. Requirements will vary widely between sites and farmers are likely to need some professional advice before deciding upon the treatment appropriate in individual situations (see Section 5.6 and Appendix C).

Since costs are shown in the budget as negative figures, incomes should be shown as positive figures. In this way the planting model/budget can be used to estimate the net cost to the farmer of establishing the farm woodland. In the example shown in Table 4.2 the farmer is shown as receiving grant from the Forestry Commission under the Woodland Grant Scheme together with the Farm Woodland Scheme payments (Section 10.1 gives details).

This Bulletin is mainly framed around the type of mixed small farm woods which farmers are expected to plant under the Farm Woodland Scheme. The operations required to establish crops under the other woodland systems covered in Section 2 vary quite extensively from those needed to create a small mixed farm woodland. The planting model examples in Appendix D indicate the work and costs required to establish these other systems, and some indications of the likely returns are given in Section 8.

While the planting model can be used to give a year by year estimate of the work input required, for detailed within year planning of labour requirement and timing Section 5.8 should be used together with the planting model to plan the work on a month by month basis.

Table 4.1 Operations checklist

This table gives an indication of the operations which are likely to be required on the different soil types listed. The number of asterisks denotes the likelihood of the operation being necessary on that particular group of soils, *** showing that it is certain, * that the operation will only sometimes be required. There may sometimes be alternatives. Brashing, for example need only be partial for fire protection alongside footpaths or to allow access for thinning, but woodland owners often choose to do a complete brashing for appearances sake or, if shooting is important, to allow access for beaters.

Although in Section 3 there are 14 soil/site types listed, only 6 are shown in this table. This is because for practical management purposes several of those shown in Section 3 may be grouped as follows:

Soft mineral soils, peaty gleys and surface water gleys, heavy soils over limestone – heavy wet soils.
Podzols and ironpans can be combined.
All the different upland bog and peat soils (which will be of limited importance in farm forestry).
Light freely drained soils over limestone can be included with well drained loamy soils.

Site type	1 Well drained loamy soils	2 Sands and gravels	3 Podzols and ironpans	4 Heavy wet soils (gleys)	5 Organic soils (peats) uplands	6 Organic soils (peats) lowland
Establishment						
Ground preparation – cultivation:						
Agricultural plough	**	**				***
Double mouldboard plough			**	***	***	
Single mouldboard plough			**			
Rip	*		***			
Scarify	**	**				
Mounding (backhoe)				***	***	**
Ground preparation – chemical:						
Grass/broadleaved weeds	***	***		*	**	***
Bracken	***	***				
Heather		***	***	**	**	
Road/track construction	*		*	***	***	
Initial drainage			*	***	***	***
Fencing	***	***	***	***	***	***
Planting	***	***	***	***	***	***
Initial fertiliser – P			***		***	
Initial fertiliser – PK	***(1)		***(2)		***	
Weeding	***	***		***	(3)	***

24

Site type	1 Well drained loamy soils	2 Sands and gravels	3 Podzols and ironpans	4 Heavy wet soils (gleys)	5 Organic soils (peats) uplands	6 Organic soils (peats) lowland
Beating up	★★★	★★★	★★★	★★★	★★★	★★★
Cleaning (4)	★	★	★	★	★★★	★
Maintenance						
General maintenance – drains, fences and roads	★★(5)	★★(5)	★★(5)	★★★	★★★	★★★
Brashing – complete	★★★	★★★	★★★		★★★	★★★
– partial	★★★	★★★	★★★	★(6)	★(6)	★★★
Pruning (hardwoods)	★★★	★★★	★★★	★★★	★★★	★★★
Fire/storm insurance	★★★	★★★	★★★	★★★	★★★	★★★

1. If chemical ground preparation has been used prior to planting it may not be necessary to weed until the year after planting.
2. If heather is present, weeding may only be necessary in year 3.
3. With good cultivation weeding is usually unnecessary.
4. Cleaning is not likely to be necessary during the first woodland rotation on sites which have been under agriculture. The exceptions are likely to be very fertile or heathland sites with seed sources (sycamore or birch trees for example) nearby.
5. Cheaper on these sites because maintenance will be limited to roads and fences only.
6. These sites will often be non-thin, except in very sheltered situations, in which case partial brashing will be unnecessary.

25

Table 4.2 Planting model example for a small farm wood

Mixed broadleaved farm wood of 3 hectares on a brown earth, formerly under improved grass.
Expenditures – negative
Revenues – positive

Operation	% of area treated	Year(s) of operation[1]	Labour £/ha	Machinery £/ha	Materials £/ha	Total cost £/ha
Establishment						
Ground preparation	100	0	-14	-18		-32
Road/track construction						
Initial drainage						
Fencing[2]	100	0	-315	-306	-30	-651
Planting	100	0	-203		-375	-578
Initial fertiliser						
Weeding[3]	100	0 to 4	-24		-5	-29
Beating-up[4]	20	2	-28		-40	-68
Grants WGS[5]	100	0				+823
Grants WGS	100	5				+235
Grants WGS	100	10				+117
FWS annual payments	100	1 to 30				+190
Maintenance						
General maintenance (drains, fences, etc.)	100	1 to F[6]	-4		-1	-5
Brashing[7]	100	20	-35			-35
Pruning[8]	100	16	-147			-147
Pruning	100	20	-147			-147
Pruning	100	28	-147			-147
Fire insurance[9]	100	0 to 25				-2
Management expenses[10]	100	-1				-35

1. The year convention adopted in planting models is that the year of planting is always described as year 0, the year before planting as year −1, 3 years after planting as year 3 and so on.

2. For the purposes of this example it has been assumed that this 3 ha wood has a perimeter of 900 metres. At £217 per 100 metre (rabbit fencing) run this implies a cost of (9 × £217/3 ha) = £651 per hectare. In areas where there are deer, more expensive fencing would be required (see page 33).

3. Because this is a fertile site it has been assumed that grass and herbaceous weeds will develop during the first growing season and need treating. This has been costed as for glyphosate (Roundup) applied with a weedwiper, to avoid any risk of contact with the trees.

4. Beating up has been costed assuming that 20% of the trees died and needed replacing.

5. Woodland Grant Scheme grants will be paid in three instalments; 70% on completion of planting, and further instalments of 20% and 10% at 5 yearly intervals thereafter (see Section 10).

6. F denotes that expenditure continues until the year of felling.

7. Brashing has been costed assuming partial brashing over the whole area to allow access for shooting.

8. Pruning is a progressive operation with never more than one-third of the crown being removed and continues until a clean bole of 6 to 8 metres has been achieved. Only those trees selected to be part of the final crop are pruned. Costing assumes that pruning will start when about 2 metres can be pruned whilst leaving two-thirds of the tree in crown, at say 16 years.

9. Insurance has been estimated assuming fire damage cover up to 25 years of age. In fact, it may often be considered unnecessary to provide fire cover for broadleaves. Following the October 1987 gale in south-east England it may be considered more prudent to hold storm damage insurance from say 25 years until the age of felling.

10. Costs of initial professional advice on plan preparation and grant application.

Table 4.3 Operation costs, quantities and guide times

(The specifications, costs and timings given are generalised and are likely to vary between individual sites. If necessary professional advice should be sought before drawing up a detailed specification for a particular site.)

Operation	Explanations		Approximate costs (costs per hectare have been rounded to nearest whole £)
Ground preparation – cultivation			
Agricultural plough	Single furrow agricultural plough with furrows pulled at the intended plant spacing (usually at 2 metres). The purpose of this operation is to enable the tree roots to be planted in the mineral soil. Where there is no humus layer on the surface, as will usually be the case with agricultural soils, or where no weed growth is present either following an agricultural crop or because the site has been chemically weeded, there will be no need to plough before planting.	1.5 man hours at £9.0 = £14 1.5 machine hours at £12.0 = £18	
	On many farms there is only a multifurrow plough available. There is no reason why this should not be used provided there are sufficient furrows to allow planting at 2 metre spacing.	total cost per treated ha = £32	
Double mouldboard plough	Double mouldboard plough pulled by a 80 bhp tracked tractor, with the furrows spaced at 2 metre intervals. Contractors would be used to carry out this operation and it would only be practical on large (over 10 hectares) areas.	2.5 man hours at £9.0 = £23 2.5 machine hours at £15.0 = £37	
		total cost per treated ha = £60	
Single mouldboard plough	Single mouldboard plough pulled by a tracked or 4xwd tractor, with the furrows spaced at 2 metre intervals. This type of plough would normally be held only by contractors.		
	Experience has shown that crops grown on ground prepared in this way are at an increased risk of windblow. However, there may still be a place for single mouldboard ploughs in small fields. The plough may be used to produce ribbons of turf which are then cut up and distributed at the appropriate spacing.	5.0 man hours at £9.0 = £45 5.0 machine hours at £15.0 = £75	
		total cost per treated ha = £120	
Rip	A mounted double ripper pulled by 4xwd tractor, usually at 2 metre spacing with the intention of breaking a pan.	6.0 man hours at £9.0 = £54 6.0 machine hours at £15.0 = £90	
		total cost per treated ha = £144	

Scarify

Scarifiers as used in woodland operations are heavy and expensive pieces of machinery used to scrape aside any brash, humus layers or vegetation, leaving a planting spot in the mineral soil exposed. If available through contractors they can provide a quicker and cheaper method of ground preparation than ploughing. Their use also has the advantage on shallow chalk soils that they can be adjusted finely enough to screef without bringing the chalk to the surface.

1.3 man hours	at £9.0	=	£12
1.3 machine hours	at £20.0	=	£26
total cost per treated ha		=	£38

Mounding (backhoe)

This treatment is a cheap alternative on heavy wet or organic soils. The backhoe is used to dig out dollops of soil or peat and deposit them in the intended planting positions, a digger bucketful being used for each tree. Through experience, costs may be substantially reduced by a long-reach excavator rather than a backhoe.

14.5 man hours	at £9.0	=	£130
14.5 machine hours	at £12.0	=	£174
total cost per treated ha		=	£304

Ground preparation – chemical

Trade names are given in brackets. Prescription for the use of herbicides is complicated and farmers should refer to the Forestry Commission Bulletin which will replace Booklet 51 or obtain professional advice before spraying. See also Section 12.

Grass/herbaceous weeds

Glyphosate (Roundup) for overall weed kill to prepare ground for planting can be sprayed using a tractor-mounted boom sprayer, and applying 1.5 litres of chemical per hectare. This treatment can be done up to 3 days before planting. Application has been costed as for tractor-mounted spraying using a 6 metre boom. For small areas (less than 0.5 hectares) use of a knapsack sprayer would be more appropriate.

0.9 man hours	at £9.0	=	£8
0.9 machine hours	at £7.5	=	£7
1.5 litres chemical	at £17.0	=	£26
total cost per treated ha		=	£41

Glyphosate (Roundup) for spot weed control to prepare ground for planting can be applied by knapsack sprayer, or by Forestry Spot Gun (a knapsack sprayer specifically designed for spot spraying). Spot weeding (treating only the one metre diameter planting spot) has the advantage of reducing the chemical cost (preparing 2500 planting spots per hectare uses 20% of the chemical required for an overall spray). Treatment rate should be at 1.5 litres per treated hectare. With any spot application treatment should be done far enough in advance of planting to allow time for the vegetation on the planting spot to die. Application has been costed as for Forestry Spot Gun.

3.5 man hours	at £7.0	=	£25
0.3 litres chemical	at £17.0	=	£5
total cost per treated ha		=	£30

Operation	Explanations	Approximate costs (costs per hectare have been rounded to nearest whole £)

Bracken

Glyphosate (Roundup) for overall bracken control to prepare ground prior to tree planting should be applied at 3 litres of chemical per treated hectare. For overall treatment, application by a tractor-mounted boom sprayer would be cheapest, and costing has been based on this method assuming a 6 metre boom.

Glyphosate should be preferred where bracken is growing with other weeds.

0.9 man hours	at £9.0 = £8
0.9 machine hours	at £7.5 = £7
3.0 litres chemical	at £17.0 = £51
total cost per treated ha	= £66

Asulam (Asulox) for overall bracken control prior to planting can be applied at 5 litres (late June/July) or 10 litres (August/early September) of chemical per treated hectare. For overall treatment application by tractor-mounted boom sprayer, or for large areas especially on uneven upland ground, contract aerial spraying would be cheapest. Costings assume a conventional hydraulic tractor-mounted sprayer with boom length depending upon the roughness of the terrain. Asulam should be preferred for pure bracken stands.

0.9 man hours	at £9.0 = £8
0.9 machine hours	at £7.5 = £7
5.0 litres chemical	at £7.0 = £35
total cost per treated ha	= £50

Heather

On exceptionally wet sites, as for instance in Northern Ireland, there may be advantage in leaving the heather to aid traction in ploughing.

The cheapest and easiest way to deal with heather before planting is to burn it before ploughing. Where this is not possible the following chemical treatments can be used:

2,4-D ester. This is available and approved for forestry use as an emulsifiable concentrate of a low volatile ester (50% w/v) under the trade names:

BASF 2,4-D Ester 480 (BASF)
Destox (Campbell (Sales))
BH 2,4-D Ester 50 (Burts & Harvey)

Application rates vary with date and soil type as follows: rates in litres chemical per hectare.

Soil type	May	June to mid August	Second half of August
Peat	10	8	10
Mineral	12	10	12

These rates of chemical would normally be applied in 200 to 300 litres of water per hectare.

Application has been costed as for knapsack sprayer.

5.5 man hours	at £7.0 = £38
10.0 litres chemical	at £3.12 = £31
total cost per treated ha	= £69

Glyphosate (Roundup) for overall heather control to prepare ground for planting should be applied at 4 litres of chemical per treated hectare on peaty soils, or 6 litres on mineral soils.

5.5 man hours	at £7.0 = £38
4.0 litres chemical	at £17.0 = £68

planted on land previously under arable or improved grass. However, they will often be a problem where woods are being restocked.

Glyphosate (Roundup) can be applied as a foliar spray at a rate of 3 to 5 litres of chemical per hectare, diluted in 200 to 300 litres of water. Application should be in June to August, and has been costed as for knapsack sprayer.

5.5 man hours	at	£7.0 =	£38
4.0 litres chemical	at	£17.0 =	£68
total cost per treated ha		=	£106

Gorse, broom and rhododendron

For rhododendron control trichlopyr (Garlon 4) should be applied as a foliar spray at a rate of 8 to 10 litres of Garlon 4 diluted in 200 to 300 litres of water per treated hectare. For gorse and broom apply 2 to 4 litres of Garlon 4 diluted in 200 to 300 litres of water per treated hectare using a knapsack sprayer. Costings are for knapsack sprayer on rhododendron. It should be recognised that the cost of this treatment may vary widely according to intensity of infestation.

5.5 man hours	at	£7.0 =	£38
9.0 litres chemical	at	£21.5 =	£194
total cost per treated ha		=	£232

Roads

On farms with dry firm ground no roads will be required, but they may be needed on heavy wet soils or organic soils.

Materials:

Clean well graded gravels or crushed stone using 3.6 tonnes per metre run.

Pipes for culverts, concrete for up to 450 mm diameter, above that use corrugated steel. Pipes come in 1 metre lengths and eight are required per culvert.

Machines (used for cutting and formation):

Excavator: will do 150 to 250 metres per week depending on site conditions and materials.

Bulldozer: will do 400 to 600 metres per week depending on site conditions and materials:

Additional machinery and labour is required for spreading and rolling surfacing materials.

Excavator formation

For the purposes of safety it is necessary to have a banksman accompany the machinery in use for these operations and this has been allowed for in the costings. Costs assume 12 metres of road per hectare.

8.8 man hours	at	£8.0 =	£70
culverts			£10
4.3 machine hours	at	£13.0 =	£56
43 tonnes materials	at	£5.5 =	£236
total cost per planted ha		=	£372

Bulldozer formation

For the purposes of safety it is necessary to have a banksman accompany the machinery in use for these operations and this has been allowed for in the costings. Costs assume 12 metres of road per hectare.

4.8 man hours	at	£8.0 =	£38
culverts			£10
2.2 machine hours	at	£20.0 =	£44
43 tonnes materials	at	£5.5 =	£236
total cost per planted ha		=	£328

Operation	Explanations	Approximate costs (costs per hectare have been rounded to nearest whole £)		
Initial drainage				
Ploughed drains	Time allows for a banksman.	4.0 man hours	at £8.0	= £32
	This will normally be carried out as an adjunct to ploughing on heavy wet or organic soils. Some hand work to tidy up drain ends and where furrows cross will also be required.	0.5 man hours	at £7.0	= £4
		2.0 machine hours	at £15.0	= £30
		total cost per treated ha		= £66
Backhoe (wheeled excavator) e.g. JCB 3X	On heavy wet agricultural soils this method may be appropriate.	10 man hours	at £8.0	= £80
		5.0 machine hours	at £9.5	= £48
		total cost per treated ha		= £128
Tracked excavator	The same comments as for wheeled excavators apply. Costs may be slightly higher especially on small sites because of the need to transport the machine to site on a low loader and the consequent setting in charge.	6.0 man hours	at £8.0	= £48
		3.0 machine hours	at £13.0	= £39
	Well drained loamy soils – 100 metres per hectare (3 hours) Heavy wet soils – 250 metres per hectare (5 hours)	total cost per treated ha		= £87
Hand drainage	This is heavy and slow work and should only be considered where the minimum of opening up is required.	8.0 man hours	at £7.0	= £56
	Costs assume 80 metres per hectare.	total cost per treated ha		= £56
Ditching machines e.g. Dondi	This is a specialist type of machine which would only be employed through a contractor. This type of machine would only be practical if a large area of soft wet or organic soil was being treated. It is unlikely to be significant in the farm woodland situation.	2.0 man hours	at £8.0	= £16
		1.0 machine hour	at £15.0	= £15
		total cost per treated ha		= £31
Fencing				
Treeshelters	Treeshelters have become popular for use with broadleaved plantings. Except when used on very small areas they are expensive by comparison with fencing because the cost remains fixed per tree. Costing assumes 1100 plants (3 metre spacing) protected by shelters per hectare.	34 man hours	at £7.0	= £238
		1100 stakes at 26p		= £286
		1100 shelters at 50p		= £550
		total cost per treated ha		= £1,074

Rabbit fencing

Cost per hectare will vary according to size and shape of the block.
To set up 100 metres:
24 treated pointed stakes (1.7m × 50 mm to 80 mm top diameter)
1 strainer (2 m × 100 mm to 130 mm top diameter)
1 strut (2 m × 80 mm to 100 mm top diameter)
2 × 50 metre rolls netting (1050 mm wide, 18 gauge, 31 mm mesh)
220 m hanging wire, spring steel (2.65 mm diameter)

15 man hours	at	£7.0	= £105
materials			= £102
1.0 machine hour	at	£10.0	= £10
total cost per 100 metres			= £217

Stock fencing

Cost per hectare will vary according to size and shape of the block.
To set up 100 metres:
24 treated pointed stakes (1.7 m × 50 mm to 100 mm top diameter)
1 strainer (2 m × 100 mm to 130 mm top diameter)
1 strut (2 m × 80 mm to 100 mm top diameter)
2 × 50 metre rolls welded or woven wire mesh
220 m hanging wire, spring steel (2.65 mm diameter)
101 m high tensile barbed wire

14 man hours	at	£7.0	= £98
materials			= £97
1.0 machine hour	at	£10.0	= £10
total cost per 100 metres			= £205

Deer fencing

Cost per hectare will vary according to size and shape of the block.
To set up 100 metres:
24 treated pointed stakes (2.5 m × 50 mm to 80 mm top diameter)
1 strainer (2.8 × 100 mm to 130 mm top diameter)
1 strut (2.5 m × 80 mm to 100 mm top diameter)
4 × 50 metre rolls welded or woven wire mesh
330 m hanging wire, spring steel (2.65 mm diameter)

25 man hours	at	£7.0	= £175
materials			= £177
1.0 machine hour	at	£10.0	= £10
total cost per 100 metres			= £362

Planting

Japanese paper pot

Planting of container grown (often Japanese paper pot) seedlings is usually limited to pines on sandy mineral soils. On these sites a special planting tool, the 'Pottiputki' can be used, although forestry planting spades are a suitable though less effective (more time consuming) substitute.

16 man hours	at	£7.0	= £112
2.5 thousand plants	at	£80.0	= £200
total cost per planted ha			= £312

Hand planting, conifer transplants

Using a planting spade with bare rooted transplants carried by the planter in a shoulder bag. Planting costs assume 2 metre spacing, i.e. 2500 plants per hectare.

20 man hours	at	£7.0	= £140
2.5 thousand plants	at	£80.0	= £200
total cost per planted ha			= £340

Hand planting, broadleaved seedlings/transplants

Using a planting spade with bare rooted transplants carried by the planter in a shoulder bag. Planting costs assume 2 metre spacing, i.e. 2500 plants per hectare.

29 man hours	at	£7.0	= £203
2.5 thousand plants	at	£150	= £375
total cost per planted ha			= £578

Operation	Explanations	Approximate costs (costs per hectare have been rounded to nearest whole £)
Hand pit planting broadleaved whips (small areas only)	Using a planting spade with bare rooted transplants carried by the planter in a shoulder bag; with extra effort being made on pit cultivation and the inclusion of peat as a backfill. Planting costs assume 2 metre spacing, i.e. 2500 per hectare, and 8 litres of mulch per tree, from 80 litre bags.	180 man hours at £7.0 = £1260 2.5 thousand plants at £180 = £450 250 bags mulch at £2.0 = £500
	This type of planting is only appropriate for small numbers of amenity trees. It is too expensive to be realistically considered for establishing a farm woodland.	total cost per planted ha = £2210
Post hole borer/semi cultivated pit planting	Using a post hole borer to make the planting holes instead of a spade, and using peat or a planting mulch as 20% of backfill. Planting costs assume 2 metre spacing, i.e. 2500 per hectare, and 8 litres of mulch per tree, from 80 litre bags.	165 man hours at £7.0 = £1155 2.5 thousand plants at £180 = £450 127 machine hours at £0.4 = £50 250 bags mulch at £2.0 = £500
	This type of planting is only appropriate for small numbers of amenity trees. It is too expensive to be realistically considered for establishing a farm woodland.	total cost per planted ha = £2155
Initial fertiliser	There are three main types of fertiliser which might be applied: P as ground rock phosphate (GRP) P as superphosphate granules P and K together in granular form	
Hand application	Except for very small areas this is expensive but it has the advantage that the fertiliser can be placed where the tree will grow. Application has been costed for P in granular form.	12 man hours at £7.0 = £84 0.3 tonnes fertiliser at £135 = £40 total cost per treated ha = £124
Tractor application	Tractor-mounted granular fertiliser spreader with rotary spinner assuming 60 kg per hectare of elemental P applied. For PK the rates would be 60 kg per ha of elemental P applied, and 100 kg per hectare of elemental K applied. Application has been costed for P in granular form.	3.0 man hours at £9.0 = £27 3.0 machine hours at £15.0 = £45 0.3 tonnes fertiliser at £135 = £40 total cost per treated ha = £112
Aerial application (helicopter)	This method is only suited for very large-scale applications. The work would normally be done by a contractor. The cost would vary according to the size of the area. Where P and K are applied it is normal to make separate runs for each because of the difficulty of mixing and achieving an even spread of the two together. Application has been costed for P in granular form.	total cost per treated ha = £100

Weeding

Manual weeding

Hand weeding is expensive and ineffective in controlling weed competition. Where possible chemical weeding should be used instead. In some circumstances, e.g. follow up of chemically treated bracken, or beside watercourses where chemicals must NOT be used, hand weeding may be necessary.

Costs vary according to the type and amount of vegetation.

Typical man hours per hectare would be as follows:

Soft grasses (*Holcus*, cocksfoot, *Molinia*) herbaceous weeds and bracken

18 man hours	at £7.0	= £126
total cost per planted ha		= £126

Coarse grasses (*Deschampsia, Calamagrostis*)

23 man hours	at £7.0	= £161
total cost per planted ha		= £161

Woody weeds

42 man hours	at £7.0	= £294
total cost per planted ha		= £294

Mechanical weeding

Although apparently cheaper, mechanical weeding is sometimes ineffective at removing competition and chemical weeding is preferable.

Costing assumes use of tractor and swipe.

3.0 man hours	at £7.0	= £21
3.0 machine hours	at £5.8	= £17
total cost per treated ha		= £38

Chemical weeding
Grass/herbaceous

Trade names are given in brackets. Prescription for the use of herbicides is complicated and farmers should refer to the Forestry Commission Bulletin which will replace Booklet 51 or obtain professional advice before spraying. See also Section 12.

Glyphosate (Roundup) can be applied by knapsack sprayer, by Forestry Spot Gun (a knapsack sprayer especially designed for spot spraying) or by wick applicator (Weedwiper) at 1.5 litres of chemical per treated hectare. Broadleaved trees are particularly sensitive to glyphospate so a guarded spray must be used.

3.5 man hours	at £7.0	= £24
0.3 litres chemical	at £17.0	= £5
total cost per treated ha		= £29

Application has been costed as for Forestry Spot Gun.

Propyzamide (Kerb by PBI or Clanex by Shell) used for spot control of most grasses. It is applied in granule form normally by hand using 'pepperpot' applicators, with the chemical being applied at 37.5 kg per treated hectare. It is only effective if applied during cold weather, and should only be used from October to December in lowland areas (it can be used until January in the uplands).

5.0 man hours	at £7.0	= £35
7.1 kg chemical	at £5.0	= £36
total cost per treated ha		= £71

Application has been costed as for 'pepperpot'.

Operation	Explanations	Approximate costs (costs per hectare have been rounded to nearest whole £)
Bracken	Glyphosate (Roundup) applied at 2 litres of chemical per treated hectare by knapsack sprayer. Broadleaved trees are particularly sensitive to glyphosate so a guarded spray should be used. Application has been costed as for knapsack sprayer.	5.5 man hours at £7.0 = £39 2.0 litres chemical at £17.0 = £34 total cost per treated ha = £73
	Asulam (Asulox) for overall bracken control for weeding applied at 5 litres of chemical per treated hectare (late June/July) or 10 litres (August/early September). Application has been costed as for knapsack sprayer.	5.5 man hours at £7.0 = £39 5.0 litres chemical at £7.0 = £35 total cost per treated ha = £74

Heather	2,4-D ester. This is available and approved for forestry use as an emulsifiable concentrate of a low volatile ester (50% w/v) under the trade names:
	  BASF 2,4-D Ester 480 (BASF)
	  Destox (Campbell (Sales))
	  BH 2,4-D Ester 50 (Burts & Harvey)
	Application rates vary with date and soil type as follows: rates in litres chemical per hectare.	

Soil type	May	June to mid August	Second half of August
Peat	10	8	10
Mineral	12	10	12

Operation	Explanations	Approximate costs
	These rates of chemical would normally be applied in 200 to 300 litres of water per hectare. Broadleaved trees are particularly sensitive to 2,4-D so a guarded spray should be used. Application has been costed as for knapsack sprayer.	5.5 man hours at £7.0 = £39 10 litres chemical at £3.12 = £31 total cost per treated ha = £70
	Glyphosate (Roundup) can be applied by knapsack sprayer at 4 litres (peaty soils) or 6 litres (mineral soils) per treated hectare. Spruces and pines are moderately tolerant to overall sprays of glyphosate after new growth has hardened off. Other species should not be sprayed and to avoid damage a guarded spray should be used. Application has been costed as for knapsack sprayer.	5.5 man hours at £7.0 = £39 4.0 litres chemical at £17.0 = £68 total cost per treated ha = £107

Forestry Commission Bulletin 80

Farm Woodland Planning

ISBN 011 710266 0

CORRECTIONS

Page 26, Table 4.2, Fencing.	*Costs for* Machinery *and* Materials *are transposed.*
Page 46, Section 5.4, Game, line 2.	*For* 'con-' *read* 'context,'.
Page 89, Table 10.1, column 3.	*Omit* '630'.
Page 117, Farm woodland advice, para. 3.	*For* 'Dean' *read* 'Devon'.
	The project office address should read: Unit 4, National School, St Thomas Road, Launceston, Cornwall. Tel. 0208 4330
Page 125, Table D.7, Year 0, column 3.	*For* '£65,000' *read* '£65 per 1000'. *For* '£40,000' *read* '£40 per 1000'.

Forestry Commission
November 1988
LONDON: HER MAJESTY'S STATIONERY OFFICE

Woody weeds

Glyphosate (Roundup) can be applied by knapsack sprayer, or by Forestry Spot Gun (a knapsack sprayer specially modified for spot applications) at a rate of 2 to 3 litres per treated hectare. As noted above, care should be taken to avoid spraying sensitive crop species.

Foliar treatment is preferable wherever the weeds are in leaf and the foliage is accessible for spraying.

Tall stems which need to be cut, and cannot for some reason be stump treated, may be allowed to regrow 1 or 2 years then resprayed.

Application has been costed as for knapsack sprayer.

5.5 man hours	at	£7.0	= £39
2.5 litres chemical	at	£17.0	= £42
total cost per treated ha			= £81

Beating up (replacing failed trees)

10% replacement

Labour costs per tree higher than normal planting because of the need to locate gaps.

In normal large-scale forestry beating up would not normally be considered for a failure rate of less than 20%. In the more intensive and smaller-scale circumstances of farm woods beating up for a failure rate as low as 10% may be contemplated. The unit cost will be greater the smaller the proportion of failed trees being replaced.

3.0 man hours	at	£7.0	= £21
0.25 thousand plants	at	£80.0	= £20
total cost per planted ha			= £41

20% replacement

4.0 man hours	at	£7.0	= £28
0.5 thousand plants	at	£80.0	= £40
total cost per planted ha			= £68

Cleaning

Mechanical-swipe

This treatment does not kill the vegetation and further cutting is likely to be required after a year or two.

3.0 man hours	at	£7.0	= £21
3.0 machine hours	at	£5.8	= £17
total cost per treated ha			= £38

Mechanical – clearing saw

This treatment does not control the vegetation permanently and further cutting is likely to be required after a year or two.

57 man hours	at	£7.0	= £399
57 machine hours	at	£0.7	= £40
total cost per treated ha			= £439

Mechanical/chemical

Note the warnings given above under ground preparation and weeding with chemicals. Using a clearing saw fitted with an attachment (Enso) which applies glyphosate (Roundup) to the cut surface as it is cut.

63 man hours	at	£7.0	= £441
63 machine hours	at	£0.7	= £44
5.0 litres chemical	at	£17.0	= £85
total cost per treated ha			= £570

Operation	Explanations	Approximate costs (costs per hectare have been rounded to nearest whole £)
Chemical	Glyphosate (Roundup) can be applied by knapsack sprayer, or by Forestry Spot Gun (a knapsack sprayer specially modified for spot application), at a rate of 2 to 3 litres per treated hectare. Broadleaved trees are particularly sensitive to glyphosate so a guarded spray must be used. Foliar treatment is preferable wherever the weeds are in leaf and the foliage is accessible for spraying. Costs per hectare are relatively low. Tall stems which need to be cut and cannot for some reason be stump treated, may be allowed to regrow 1 or 2 years then sprayed. Application has been costed as for knapsack sprayer.	8.0 man hours at £7.0 = £56 2.5 litres chemical at £17.0 = £42 total cost per treated ha = £98
Maintenance	Some maintenance will be required about every 5 years for roads, drains and fences. Periodic weed control on the road pavement will be required. Total cost is about £25 per hectare, i.e. £5 per hectare per year.	0.6 man hours at £7.0 = £4 materials = £1 total cost per planted ha = £5 per year
Brashing – partial	Partial brashing may be to provide inspection racks or for shooting. If for the latter the charge should be against the shooting account.	5.0 man hours at £7.0 = £35 total cost per planted ha = £35
– complete	This may be done for appearance, e.g. near to the farmhouse or a recreation facility.	30 man hours at £7.0 = £210 total cost per planted ha = £210
Pruning and high pruning	This will only be done for the better stems in high grade broadleaved crops. 300 trees per hectare at 50p per tree, normally pruning up to a maximum of 6 metres.	21 man hours at £7.0 = £147 total cost per planted ha = £147
Fire/storm insurance	It is possible to insure woodland against storm damage and fire. The costs of insurance vary according to the age of the crop and whether it is conifer or broadleaved. As age increases total cover increases but premium per £100 of cover diminishes. The premium tends to be cheaper for broadleaves. Costs are quoted assuming cover £2500 per hectare at £0.2 per £100 (see Section 5.7)	total cost per planted ha = £5 per year

Section 5
Miscellaneous

Section 5 Miscellaneous

5.1 Weed Control and Costs

The need to weed

The main object of weeding, which might be necessary for the first 4 to 5 years following planting, is to secure successful establishment and rapid early growth of the crop. This is achieved by the elimination of competition for moisture, nutrients and light. The most effective way to do this is either by cultivation, herbicide application or mulching. Any form of cutting, which might have to be repeated during the season, will only reduce competition for light. On grassy sites cutting sustains the grass vigour. This often results in drier soils, thus reducing tree height growth through lack of moisture. It is therefore important particularly during the period of April to June and on grassy sites that at least a one metre spot or band free of vegetation is created around the tree, in order to reduce competition for moisture and nutrients.

Weeding methods

Preliminary cultivation by ploughing is the main method of weed control on most upland afforestation sites and if planting is prompt and successful no other weed control will be necessary. On very fertile and weedy woodland sites, even after cultivation, some form of weed control will be required. This is likely to be true for all farm woods in the lowlands.

It is recommended that on sites which have not been under regular cultivation where there are weeds such as bracken, gorse or rhododendron, which are difficult to control, these should be treated prior to planting. These are not likely to be present where farm woods are being planted on arable or improved grass but may occur in upland or rough grazing sites. The tree crop will restrict flexibility in timing and rate of herbicide application unless the trees are protected.

Where it is unsuitable to use herbicides, e.g. near watercourses, mulching (using plastic mats or split fertiliser bags for example), should be considered. Cutting should be a last resort.

Because of their slower growth rate, broadleaved trees generally require weeding for longer than conifers. They are also more susceptible to damage by herbicide. However, the use of treeshelters can give protection against damage during spraying and enhance early growth. Shelters do little to reduce weed competition particularly on grassy sites and should not be regarded as a substitute for proper weed control.

Herbicides

The range of herbicides approved for forestry is not as wide as that used in agriculture. The choice of herbicide will primarily depend upon the weed species to be controlled. Other considerations are species of tree, whether the herbicide application is pre- or post-planting, time of year, soil type and application method. Figure 5.1 illustrates the main weed types together with the appropriate herbicides and timing of application. The list of herbicides is not exhaustive and there are other suitable approved herbicides available. The information in Figure 5.1 is of a very general nature. Details essential to effective treatment are to be found in the appropriate sections of the Forestry Commission Bulletin which is in preparation to replace Booklet 51 *The use of herbicides in the forest*. All herbicides and other pesticides used in woodlands are subject to the Control of Pesticides Regulations, 1986. (See Section 12.)

Application methods

When selecting the application method the following points should be considered:

1. the extent of the target area which needs to be controlled;
2. the cost of the operation and any logistic problems together with environmental and aesthetic impact of the operation; and
3. the need to avoid damaging wildlife and other environmental interests through indiscriminate or careless application or during disposal of containers and surplus herbicide.

Overall application is appropriate only where the control of vegetation in spots or bands is insufficient, such as for control of bracken, gorse and rhododendron.

For overall application, tractor-mounted boom sprayers will give greater outputs per man day and improved operator working conditions than hand-held applicators such as low speed rotary atomisers or knapsack sprayers which treat between a 1- or 2-metre swathe at each pass over low vegetation. However, long booms are only suitable for use on smooth

41

Guide to use of Herbicides in Farm Woods

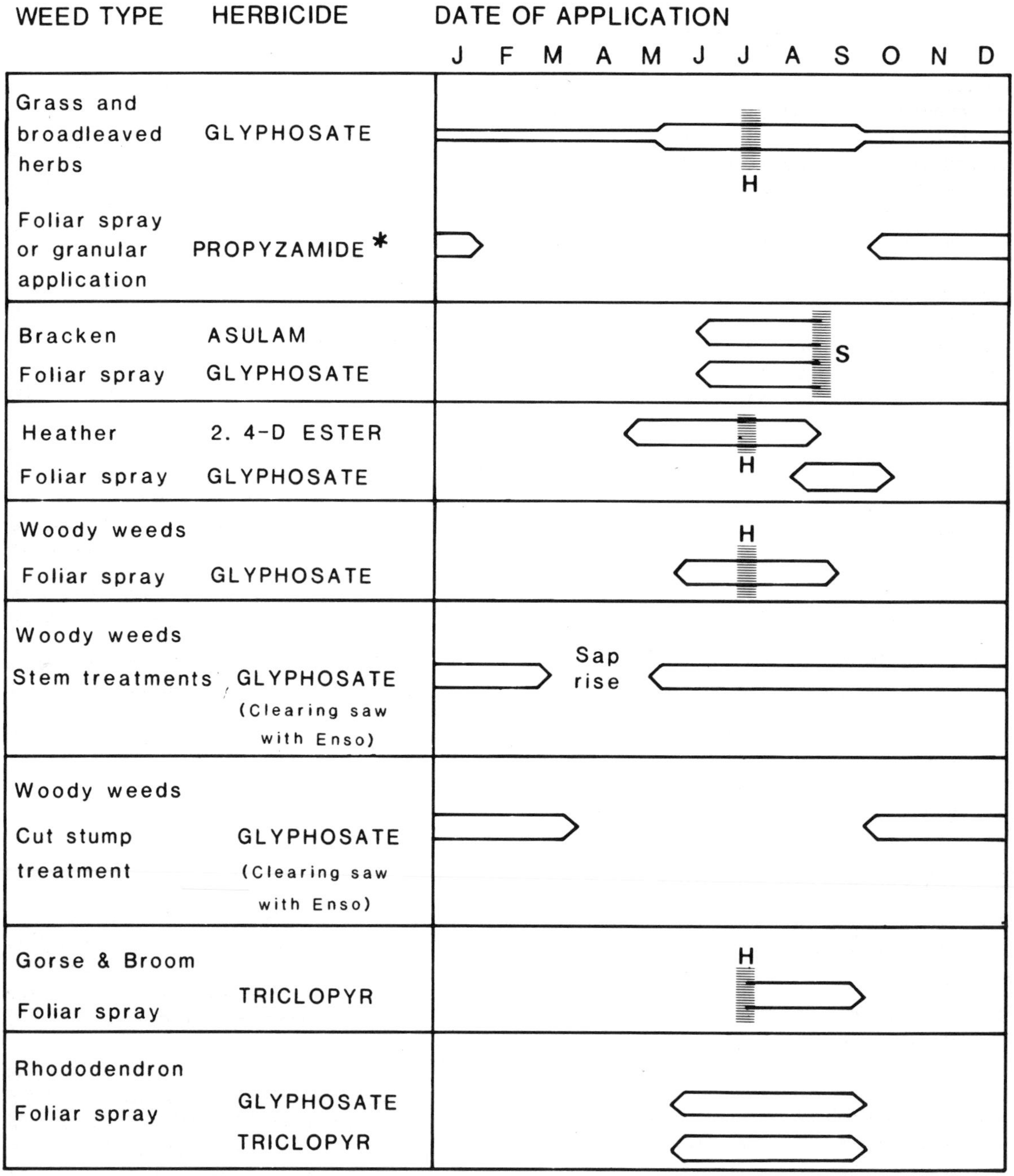

WEED TYPE	HERBICIDE	DATE OF APPLICATION

Figure 5.1

* In upland Britain use can be extended to January

H = Earliest date of hardening-off of crop

S = Commencement of senescence of weeds

ground because of the difficulty of maintaining a consistent height between the spray nozzle and the vegetation if the tractor is yawing and pitching on rough ground. On most agricultural sites being planted under the Farm Woodland Scheme this should not be a problem.

Where overall application is inappropriate the choice of applicator will depend upon whether a spot or band treatment is required and sensitivity of the crop tree to the herbicide. For band application where the crop trees will tolerate overall spray, and terrain permits, a tractor-mounted boom sprayer, adapted for band application, is the first choice. Hand-held low speed rotary atomisers or knapsack sprayers are an alternative. Where the crop trees will not tolerate the herbicide and vegetation is low enough, a knapsack sprayer with the nozzle guarded is the only suitable applicator but a pass either side of the row will be required. For spot application where trees are herbicide tolerant, either a knapsack sprayer fitted with a cone nozzle or the Forestry Spot Gun (a knapsack sprayer specially developed for spot application) is usually used.

The advantages of spot sprayers are accuracy of dose and spot diameter together with the ease of operation. In very herbicide sensitive crops or where guards do not give adequate protection, the rope wick applicators will give good vegetation control providing that the flow to and cleanliness of the wick are maintained.

Granular herbicides are applied by a gravity feed band applicator or by the 'pepperpot' for spot application.

Costs and outputs

Costs can vary considerably depending upon whether application is complete, band or spot, and on terrain, row spacing and ease of locating the trees.

With, for example, trees planted at 2 by 2 metre spacing the herbicide costs for weeding a gross area are in the proportion:

general spray overall	100%
1 metre band spray	50%
1 metre diameter spot	20%

Tractor output will depend upon boom width and forward speed – this is often governed by the roughness of ground conditions.

$$\text{min/ha} = \frac{10\ 000}{\substack{\text{Forward speed} \times \text{Swathe width} \\ \text{(metres/minute)} \quad \text{(metres)}}} \times 1.43$$

Only very broad guidance can be given for outputs using hand-held applicators as working conditions

cover a wide range of sites, vegetation types, vigour and planting spacing. Table 5.1 illustrates this.

Table 5.1 Hand-held applicator output guide times

	Easy[1] (min/ha)	Difficult[2] (min/ha)
	Minutes per treated hectare	
Knapsack (guarded spray) SPOT	437	677
(unguarded) COMPLETE	250	338
Low speed rotary atomisers		
BAND	195	480
COMPLETE	260	468
Forestry Spot Gun (spot application)		
SPOT	106	213
Rope wick applicators[3]		
SPOT	308	771
Pepperpot SPOT	230	345

Notes: 1 Easy conditions. Relatively flat, walking speed during application in region of 60 metres per minute, trees easy to locate.
2 Difficult conditions. Moderate − steep slopes, walking speed during application in region of 30 metres per minute, trees difficult to locate.
3 Walking speed during application: trees easy to locate − 20 metres per minute, trees difficult to locate − 8 metres per minute.

As a comparison hand cutting of the vegetation would range between 590−2160 minutes per hectare.

Mulching, the laying and fixing of a metre square plastic mat can take between 70−170 minutes per 100 mats.

5.2 Roads and Tracks

The width and specification of farm/forestry roads and tracks will depend on the required use, topography, underlying materials and availability of road making material. All these factors will obviously affect the cost as will the degree of culverting and bridge building required.

Farm/field access roads and tracks are normally in the region of 3 metres wide involving excavation down to hard formation followed by laying 150–400 mm of crushed stone which is blinded and rolled. Costs for tracks of this type range from £6 to £18 per linear metre inclusive of small culverts. Suitably sized ditches to outfalls and parallel to verges will improve the long-term performance of roads and tracks. Under most circumstances, farm roads and tracks of this type will be adequate for meeting the demands for access to small farm woodlands, although sharp and narrow

Road cross section in level ground

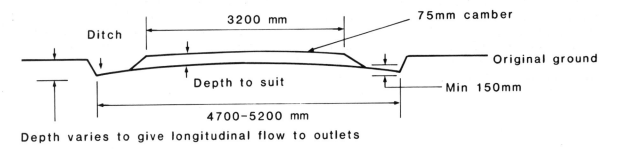

Figure 5.2 Road cross section in level ground.

Road cross section cut and fill

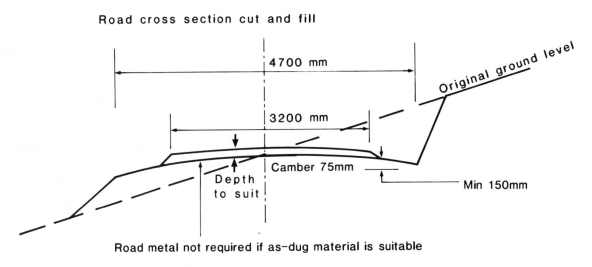

Figure 5.3 Road cross section cut and fill.

bends should be avoided as these may present difficulties for access by heavy vehicles.

Intermediate specification tracks and agricultural hill roads are normally cut and fill using suitable material from borrow pits along the route. Little or no imported materials should be necessary and approximate costs would vary between £5–£6 per linear metre excluding culverts to £15 per linear metre inclusive of small culverts but again excluding bridges. Three hundred millimetre diameter culverts cost in the region of £13 per linear metre of culvert.

High specification roads capable of carrying heavy forestry vehicles and machinery are normally 3.2 m wide. The ground should be cut back to hard formation level with bottoming laid from 200 mm to 400 mm thick. The formation width excavated will increase as the depth of bottoming increases and should

also allow for drainage as shown in Figures 5.2 and 5.3, but is normally between 4.7 m and 5.7 m. The surface may require blinding and is normally rolled to a camber of 75 to 90 mm and this changes to a crossfall of 150–190 mm where the road is on a steep side slope. The road width can increase to 5.9 m at sharp curves with a minimum radius of 15 metres. Turning and passing places should be provided as necessary. This type of road costs approximately £30 per linear metre including small culverts but excluding bridges.

It will be obvious that if deep peat involving the use of geotextile fabric or excessive depths of bottoming, rock cutting/blasting and drainage works, and the need for large culverts or bridges, are involved in the building of a road the cost per linear metre will be dramatically affected. However, by careful choice of route it is sometimes possible to minimise the need for those costly items. The use of a professional engineer with appropriate experience should be considered.

In general terms labour would account for something in the order of 25–35 per cent of the cost of high specification roads and 18–23 per cent of the cost of intermediate specification roads. These are very broad indicators as much will depend on the actual work to be carried out and the type of plant employed to do it, not least the haulage distances involved in disposing of soil and/or importing bottoming, etc. Guideline costs are given in Table 5.2.

Table 5.2. Guideline costs for farm road construction

1. *Excavate to formation level and compact ground*
Cost/m²★ varies from £0.90 in Figure 5.2 to £1.80 in Figure 5.3.

2. *Cost of quarried rock*
Cost/m² ex quarry £1.70 – £2.55 for 200 mm depth.
                  £3.60 – £5.40 for 400 mm depth.

Transport costs

Distance to quarry (one way)	Cost/m² 200 mm	Cost/m² 400 mm
8 km (5 mls)	£0.43	£0.90
16 km (10 mls)	£0.65	£1.35
24 km (15 mls)	£0.86	£1.80

3. *Cost of gravel from own pit*
Cost/m² to excavate load and transport material up to 3 km (2 miles).
a. for 200 mm deep pavement £0.44
b. for 400 mm deep pavement £0.88

4. *Cost for laying and compacting pavement*
a. for 200 m deep pavement £0.90/m²
b. for 400 m deep pavement £1.80/m²

5. *Cost of cut and fill road in suitable material*
Cost to cut, fill and compact road on mild crossfall without rock excavation or need for imported material £2.10/m²

6. *Cost of concrete road* (materials only) £9.00/m²

7. *Cost of culverts for road* (materials only)
£13/linear m of culvert

8. *Cattle grids* material only £900 each

★ Unit is m² of finished road surface.

Grants may be available under the AIS(EC) (Agricultural Improvement Scheme (European Community)) for farm roads and tracks. The grant rate in the LFAs (Less Favoured Areas) is 20 per cent and in the non LFAs is 15 per cent. Claims may be paid on the reasonable actual costs incurred or on standard costs, details of which vary from time to time and which are available from the local Ministry or Departmental office. Any items claimable under the AIS(EC) must of course form part of an approved improvement plan and grant rates, grant ceilings and eligible items may vary from time to time.

Under some circumstances such as in National Scenic Areas the development of farm tracks is controlled, although vehicle tracks required for afforestation schemes are accepted. Attention is drawn to these regulations in Section 11.4.

5.3 Arboricultural Costs

Isolated trees standing in hedgerows and around farm buildings can be an asset, not simply as an amenity, but in terms of their timber value. Properly cared for, these trees can sometimes yield veneer quality logs. Unfortunately such trees are frequently regarded as a nuisance and they can prove very expensive to manage. This need not be the case.

Where there is injury to people or damage to property as a result of a tree breaking or blowing over, both the courts and the insurance companies will consider there has been negligence if the tree had not been inspected regularly. Such an inspection can be by the owner, his tenant or agent. Whoever inspects the trees should have some knowledge of signs of structural weakness and symptoms of declining vigour. These are described in *The recognition of hazardous trees*, a free leaflet available from the Forestry Commission. Where signs of ill health or structural weakness are found then remedial steps should be taken to make the trees safe – this may involve seeking a detailed report from an arboriculturist before a decision is taken about the appropriate treatment for the tree. (The Arboricultural Association will supply free of charge a copy of their Directory of Consultants and Contractors. See Appendix C.)

In open fields where there is nothing that can be damaged, felling trees is relatively straightforward. The actual cost of felling the tree may be as low as £10–£20, but to this must be added the cost of disposal of the material arising. Cutting and burning the lop and top from an average hedgerow tree can take a whole day and may cost another £40–£60. If the trunk is of good quality and can be added to other timber being sold from the estate, then income may offset the cost of felling and clearance of the site; £50–£80 may appear expensive to fell a single tree in an open situation, but the work is hazardous, requiring skill and experience in felling. Failure to recognise defects and understand the way in which a tree may fall can lead to serious risks. People have been killed because of their ignorance of the skills needed for tree felling. For example, it is not sufficient to fasten a tractor to the tree to direct the fall because agricultural tractors will commonly fail to provide sufficient drawbar pull to be able to safely counter the weight of the majority of hedgerow trees.

Removal of low branches or weak structures from hedgerow trees has sometimes been achieved by an operative with a chain saw standing in a tractor mounted bucket. This method may be tempting, but it is potentially extremely dangerous for the operator and the tractor, and must not be attempted. The initial cost of DIY pruning is undoubtedly cheap when compared with employing an equipped contractor who adopts safe working practices, but accidents can prove extremely costly. (Costs will depend on quantity of work, but a likely minimum charge of £40 may be expected.) Trees close to buildings require a very high degree of skill and safety equipment if they are to be removed without causing damage to people and property during the operation. A specialist tree surgeon should be able to prune out branches which overhang buildings and remove whole trees from close to buildings without causing any damage. The care and skill needed for these operations close to buildings will cost more than a similar operation in a field. How much more will depend on the position, size of tree and amount of additional handling to dispose of the lop and top. Costs for tree work close to buildings frequently run into hundreds of pounds.

The costs of these operations should not preclude individual trees and clumps of trees being planted for amenity around a farm. Careful planning and siting of trees can minimise future problems. Furthermore, selection of trees of known timber properties combined with long-term tree management to optimise the quality of the timber should permit farmers to develop a valuable resource to be marketed with other farm timber.

Reference

FORESTRY COMMISSION (1988). *The recognition of hazardous trees*. Forestry Commission leaflet (free). Available from Forest Research Station, Alice Holt Lodge, Wrecclesham, Farnham, Surrey GU10 4LH.

5.4 Sporting Revenue and Costs

Game

The most conspicuous non-timber revenue available from woodlands, especially in a farm woodland con-

is the rent *income* from letting game shooting. This can be of disproportionate value compared with the amount of woodland planted because a series of small woods of suitable design strategically placed may lift not just the rental value of the land occupied by woodland but that of the whole farm or estate (McCall, 1986). The following example is indicative of the scale of these effects.

Comparison of the capital value and sporting rental on a 400 ha farm with and without well designed shooting coverts

1. Capital value including sporting rights (a viable driven pheasant shoot).

Bare arable farm	@ £2,500/ha = £1,000,000	for the whole farm
Farm with 10 coverts of one hectare each	@ £3,100/ha = £1,240,000	

Thus the additional value arising from 10 hectacres of woodland is £240,000. Each hectacre of woodland therefore adds £24,000 to the capital value of the farm which has game coverts. In this example 2.5 per cent of the farm area planted with game coverts is increasing its capital value by 24 per cent.

2. Sporting rent

Bare arable farm	@ £2.50/ha = £1,000	for the whole farm
Farm with 10 coverts of one hectare each	@ £7.50/ha = £3,000	

Thus the value of 10 hectares of game covert is £2,000 per year, and each hectare of woodland is adding £200 a year to the farm income from sporting rent.

Provided that the woodland is sited, designed and planted correctly its sporting value can be obtained within a few years so that the increased revenue is available throughout most of the rotation. Sporting rents vary in different parts of the country and Table 5.3 gives an indication of the likely improvements in the rental value produced by judicious planting on arable farmland.

Table 5.3 Game Shooting Rentals (open market values assuming reasonable unit size – 60 ha or more) £/ha

	Open Farmland	Farmland with 2 to 10% woodland sited, designed and managed for good game producing, holding, shooting habitat.
Home Counties	2.50	12.50
150 km range of London or large Southern City	1.25 to 1.90	5.00 to 7.50
Welsh Country/ Welsh Borders	1.25	2.50 to 5.00
Scottish Lowlands	Thought to be similar to Wales, but significantly depressed due to high and unavoidable sporting rates in Scotland	
Northern Ireland	0.50 to 0.75	7.50 to 10.00

Source: Ian McCall, The Game Conservancy Advisory Service.

Factors determining value of smaller woods for game shooting

Woods, copses, spinneys and belts of 1 to 5 hectares are generally the most valuable for game and shooting. Part of the reason for this is because the pheasant, like so many other wildlife species, is primarily a bird of the edge, in this case woodland edge.

A belt is in many ways the ideal shape because there is a high ratio of edge to area (see Figure 5.4). Provided there is adequate width to offer warmth for birds, such a shape is also excellent for shooting in that, whether walking up or driving, a few individual guns or beaters can show every bird with the greatest of ease. However, care needs to be taken when siting belts so that they can show high birds by making the best use of any contours and also that they complement the natural landscape from a visual point of view.

Siting and holding capacity

The potential of woods as shooting coverts is determined by their suitability for holding game in late autumn and throughout the winter months, together with the opportunity they offer to show high pheasants. Pure broadleaved woodlands with no shrub cover and no provision of marginal shelter, once the leaf has fallen in November, are as inhospitable to game as old dark, dank conifers. In fact, once past the thicket stage it is mixed woodland that is regularly managed

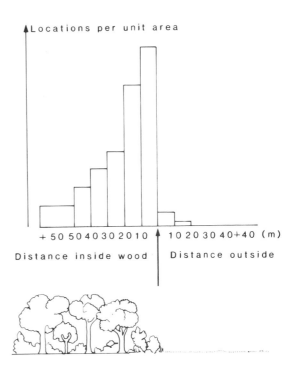

Pheasant use of woodland edges

Figure 5.4 Pheasant use of woodland edges.

and thinned that usually provides the best pheasant holding habitat.

Again recent research suggests that pheasant use of various woodland types in order of preference is as follows.

Pheasant winter habitat selection
1. Managed traditional coppice
2. Young mixed conifer/broadleaved woodland
3. Broadleaved woodland, light canopied with shrub layer
4. Mature broadleaved heavy canopy with bare floor
5. Mature conifer heavy canopy with bare floor

Technical advice on all aspects of game conservation and shoot management including woodland siting, planting and design, is available from the Game Conservancy Ltd. (See Appendix C.)

References

GAME CONSERVANCY (1981). *Woodlands for pheasants*. Game Conservancy Booklet No 15. The Game Conservancy, Fordingbridge.

McCALL, I. (1986). The economics of managing farm woodland for game. *Timber Grower*, Autumn 1986, 19–20.

Table 5.4. Producing game shooting costs/income − actual average cost/1000 birds shot from 50 shoots

Taken from the Game Conservancy's Game Shooting Cost Analysis 1986/87 season. Applies to pheasant but does not vary greatly for partridge or mallard.

INPUTS		Figures rounded off and in £s
Fixed costs		
Rent inc. *rates* range £0.50−£4.00 per acre)		1,000
Keeping		
Wages	6,000	
Housing	750	
Transport	1,000	
Dogs	250	8,000
Clothing, cartridges, etc. }		
Equipment		
Total cost of major capital items over 5 years e.g. pens, traps, etc., and costed at 20% per annum		200
Variable costs		
Restocking		
Either a. Home bred eggs collected or bought in inc. laying pen, food, incubator costs, etc.		Lower
or b. Purchasing day old chicks inc. cost, food, heating, vet and medication	2,500	
or c. Purchasing 6/7 week old poults	Higher	
		2,500
Post release feed		
Pellets }		
Wheat }		
Straw }		1,600
Game crops £100−£250 per acre rent and cost of establishment		500
Beaters/pickers-up at £10/man/day and £12/man/day respectively		1,200
	Gross cost	£15,000
OUTPUT		
Sale of game, inc. surplus stock, rabbits, etc.		1,500
	Nett cost	£13,500

Margin over production costs is only achieved if selling shooting at an overall price above £13.50/bird. Letting shooting can be i. to a syndicate of friends helping to cover costs or ii. by the day to a team of guns when VAT may be applicable. These figures are based on an average recovery just in excess of 50% including wild birds and immigrants.

Deer in farm woods

Establishment

Establishing small woodlands where deer are present involves careful planning before the trees are planted to avoid serious damage, coupled with an assessment of the possible benefits of control. In the conditions applying over most of the UK at present, the density of deer over the boundary is likely to be more than sufficient to replace culled animals very quickly, and the subsequent settlement of territorial and heirarchical claims may in fact make the damage worse, especially in the case of roe deer.

Protection measures in the establishment phase are expensive, but later, or in the case of larger woodlands of mixed age, these costs can be offset by managing the deer as a woodland asset, with the marketing of venison and of the stalking rights being done as you would for timber and pheasant shooting.

The objects of management

1. Reduce damage.
2. Maintain a healthy herd of deer within the natural capacity of the woods.
3. Balance costs by marketing:
   a. venison;
   b. sport.

Income

Income from deer starts from Year 1, and is correspondingly valuable compared to the return from timber, which may carry interest charges on the establishment costs for 40 years before any significant income is received. In farm woodlands, which are usually small and diverse, the returns, especially with the additions of income from letting, can be considerable. Naturally, the occupier must not lose control, so supervision is needed.

Densities of roe deer in small farm woods are proportionately very much higher than in large areas of forestry. A small one or two hectare wood surrounded by fields can provide cover for a family of roe so that spring time densities in farm woods in the south of England could reach one roe per one to two hectares of woodland.

These can be maintained as a stable population by shooting 35 per cent of the bucks in the proportion of six young:two middle-aged:two old bucks, and 40 per cent of the does each year.

In many areas the population is largely uncontrolled and the effect of shooting will be to provide space for incoming animals. In these circumstances much higher numbers might be shot without apparently affecting the population on the farm.

Sporting income can be derived by letting the right to shoot the middle-aged and old bucks on a day permit basis.

The rates for this are:

England £75–£100 per buck
Scotland £50–£75 per buck

The proportion of bucks shootable on this basis is small and might for example result in three to four bucks per farm. These shooting charges do not include the value of the venison. Unless farmers are registered as game dealers they must sell their venison to a game dealer (Deer Act, 1980 and Deer Scotland Act 1959 as amended in 1982). The current market price is between £1.80 and £2.00 per kg for roe venison.

Average weights for farm shot roe are likely to be:

England 15 kg
Scotland 12 kg

Income from stalking should not be sought regardless of good deer management. In many cases professional advice on deer is worth while before the commencement of any planting scheme, or when contemplating letting.

Stalkers

Individual farmers are unlikely to have a sufficiently large area of woodland to make commercial stalking viable unless they form a syndicate with neighbouring owners. The following section should be read with this in mind and where individual farmers wish to retain their independence the use of part-time amateur stalkers, subject to safeguards, should be considered. Among the safeguards necessary are to ensure that the stalker is adequately covered for third party insurance, and that he is experienced, safe and reliable.

Where the woodland area is small, part-time amateur stalkers can play a vital part in limiting damage, and producing a crop of venison.

On larger estates with a high population of roe deer, a full-time stalker may be justified, or two estates may combine to take up his capacity. Quantifying the value of his work in preventing damage is, of course, very difficult. Disregarding this vital element of his work, costs can only be balanced by letting. Where a gamekeeper is employed, he may be the best man to train in deer control. However, care must be taken to avoid an overlap of duties. This is best achieved by producing a seasonal work calendar (see Table 5.5).

Costs for employing a full-time stalker/keeper including wages, employers' National Insurance Contribution and overheads will be £7,000 to £8,000 and transport and material costs will be £2,500 to £4,000.

Letting stalking

Letting stalking as a concession to a sporting agent needs to be approached with caution. The loss of control often proves to be more of a nuisance than an asset.

Stalking is labour-intensive, and takes place at unsocial hours. Good men, amateur or professional, are valuable, and deserve support if their time is to be well spent. The fixed costs of equipment, such as the rifle, binoculars, and high seats are minimal in comparison to the time factor. No useful purpose is served by penny-pinching on these items.

Table 5.5 Seasonal work calendar for a full-time keeper/stalker

Month

ESSENTIAL DUTIES	A	M	J	J	A	S	O	N	D	J	F	M
Roe bucks	——	——	——	—	—							
Roe does							——	——	——	——	——	
Visitor stalkers		—		—								
Rearing field	——	——	——									
Poults release, feeding			——	——	——	——						
Game shooting							——	——	——	——		
Squirrel control	——	——										
Rabbit control								——	——	——	——	——

Where duties conflict, planning is needed to avoid overloading the man. Either provide help, or re-phase the duties.

Training

Training courses for stalkers are run every year by The British Deer Society and The Game Conservancy.

References

PRIOR, R. (1983). *Trees and deer*. Batsford, London.
PRIOR, R. (1987). *Roe stalking*. Game Conservancy Guide No. 24. The Game Conservancy, Fordingbridge.

5.5 Recreation

Farmers may consider developing the recreation potential of their farm woodlands for many reasons, for public enjoyment, as a business venture or to manage and control existing recreational use. In all cases it is likely that the whole farm will be considered, and the woodlands will form just one part of the overall plan.

Recreation is an activity for which farmers can create additional opportunities through co-operation with neighbouring farmers and landowners in the development of joint schemes.

There are many potential sources of advice and grant aid for recreational developments, and grant aid may be available for market research and feasibility studies through the Agricultural Departments' Farm Diversification Scheme. Initial approaches could be made through local authority planners, rural enterprise advisers of the Agricultural Departments, Countryside Commissions, Sports Councils, Regional Development Boards, Tourist Boards or COSIRA depending on the type of development concerned. It is essential that advice is sought from local planning authorities at the earliest stage in planning recreational development.

Recreation potential is generally greater in existing woodland than in areas of new planting. Mature woodland, or woodland with a diverse structure of tree crops of different ages, open areas and rides, and additional features such as water, is particularly suitable for developing recreation.

It is unlikely that farmers will be able to generate significant income from farm woodlands in isolation, but some activities benefit from a woodland setting. Woodlands can be valuable additions to farm visitor trails and can form part of a pony-trekking/riding circuit if tracks and rides are suitable. Woodland also provides a pleasant setting for many of the informal recreational activities often associated with farm holidays or bed and breakfast accommodation. It is the ideal setting for survival/war games and there is great demand for expansion of these facilities in some areas, particularly near large urban centres. Woodland absorbs sound to some extent and can be used as a screen for other activities such as clay pigeon shooting or motor cycling.

With all recreational use, the marketing of the facility is crucial to the financial success.

Wherever public access to woodland is encouraged through the provision of facilities, or there is access from public rights of way, it is important to consider all aspects of legal liability. Farmers must ensure that they have adequate insurance cover for public liability, have any necessary planning permission for recreational use, and ensure high safety standards. If in doubt about the safety measures required, then the Health and Safety Executive should be consulted. See also Section 5.3 'Arboricultural Costs' concerning legal aspects of unsafe trees. Further useful information on woodland recreation is provided in Irving (1985).

Reference

IRVING, J. A. (1985). *The public in your woods*. The Land Decade Educational Council; Packard Publishing, Chichester.

5.6 Professional Management Expenses

Farm woods are by their nature unlikely to be very large in area, indeed the Farm Woodland Scheme sets a top limit of 40 hectares for each enterprise. For that reason it is only likely to be financially worthwhile for a farmer to seek professional advice on a periodic, rather than a regular basis. A greater management advisory input may become worthwhile where groups of farmers organise themselves into some type of woodland co-operative, thereby increasing the area being managed.

Professional advice is available on all aspects of the management of farm woodlands (see Appendix C).

Where regular advice is provided, the charges are normally based either on the area of the woods or the time and expenses incurred. On small woodlands this might cost up to £15 per hectare per annum. Periodic advisory visits are likely to be charged on a time and expenses basis, but if combined with some contracting work within the woods, the costs of such visits may be reduced. While there are obvious attractions at first sight in minimising expenditure on professional advice, it is important to recognise that where the object of management of the woodlands is to maximise the financial yield, this is not often achieved simply by minimising expenditure over the life of the tree crop. Professional management advice can save money over the long term.

Where a farmer manages his own woodland it is possible to consider the cost of his time spent in terms of its opportunity cost. That is in terms of the most profitable alternative activity upon which he could have been spending his time.

5.7 Insurance

Farm woods may be insured in the same way as any other property and there are a number of (two or possibly three) firms specialising in this type of insurance cover. (A list of companies dealing with woodland insurance can, if necessary, be sought from the Institute of Chartered Foresters or The Royal Institution of Chartered Surveyors.)

Woodlands can normally be insured against damage by fire and wind. Generally all of an owner's woods have to be included within the insurance policy. This allows the company to offset the risk on the most vulnerable plantations against those less at risk.

There are variations in the principles involved in the insurance policies available. Premiums are normally charged as a percentage of the plantation value, the latter being on a predetermined scale set by the insurers, or agreed between the owner and the insurers. In some schemes the plantation valuation carries an additional sum to cover the cost of site clearance in the event of a fire or windblow. This basis of valuation is applied for the period until the wood starts to produce utilisable timber, and thereafter woods are often insured at site market or devastation value; that is the value of the timber net of harvesting cost.

The percentages used to determine the premiums can vary according to the crop type and age because of the different risks involved. The rates shown in Table 5.6 give some indication of current premium levels when crops are at their most vulnerable to either fire or windblow damage.

Table 5.6 Insurance premium rates

		Premium as % of insured value
Fire Cover	Broadleaved plantations	0.06
	Mixed plantations (not more than 50% conifer)	0.11
	Larch plantations	0.11
	Conifer plantations	0.13
Storm Damage	All plantations	0.16

The premiums for storm damage can be expected to rise in the wake of the October 1987 gale in south-east England.

Where both fire and windblow cover is required the premium rates are normally additive, but some discount may be offered in taking out both.

Table 5.7 gives an indication of one insurer's scale of plantation values on which premium may be based as at December 1987.

Although site market or devastation value is commonly used in woodland insurance, for investors this value will be much lower than the expectation value right up until shortly before the economic rotation age. Thus once the crop has grown beyond the establishment stage it may become appropriate to insure the crop on agreed expectation value; or to cover the difference between what the owner actually gets for his blown timber and expectation value. The latter should take into account the additional cost of clearance.

Third party cover is often very cheap or in some schemes is included free of charge.

Terms and conditions vary between insurers, and farmers may be able to negotiate if their own view on valuation varies from that proposed by the insurers, or according to their willingness to limit liability, or accept an excess.

Table 5.7 An insurer's scale of plantation values

Age of crop	England and S Wales	Scotland and Mid Wales
Years	£/hectare	£/hectare
1	704	352
2	792	440
3	880	528
4	968	616
5	1,056	704
6	1,144	792
7	1,232	880
8	1,320	968
9	1,408	1,056
10	1,496	1,144
11	1,584	1,232
12	1,672	1,320
13	1,760	1,408
14	1,848	1,496
15	1,936	1,584
16	2,024	1,672
17	2,112	1,760
18	2,200	1,848
19	2,288	1,936
20	2,376	2,024
21	2,464	2,112
22	2,552	2,200
23	2,640	2,288
24	2,728	2,376
25	2,816	2,464

25+At agreed valuation, either site market value or expectation value.

Source: Stewart Wrightson, Dundee.

5.8 Seasonal Requirements for Woodland Work

A great deal of work in farm woodlands can be done in agriculturally slack periods. Some operations, however, have critical timing and have to be fitted in even if this means employing off-farm labour (see Table 5.8). Some operations need specialised safety equipment and training – see Section 12.

Table 5.8 Seasonal requirements for woodland operations

Operation	D	J	F	M	A	M	J	J	A	S	O	N
Ground preparation [1] including ploughing scarifying etc	·	·	·	—	—	·	·	·	—	—	—	—
Drainage		—	—	—	—	—	—	—	—	—	—	—
Fencing		—	—	—	—	—	—	—	—	—	—	—
Planting [2] including beating up	·	·	·	—	—	—	·					—
Weeding [3] Propyzamide	—	—	—	—	·	·						
Glyphosate					·	·	·	—	—	—	—	·
Cleaning		—	—	—	—	—	—	—	—	—	—	—
Pruning Cherry								—	—	—		
Walnut									—	—	—	·
Others		—	—					—	—	—	—	—
Brashing		—	—	—	—	—	—	—	—	—	—	—
Thinning		—	—	—	—	—	—	—	—	—	—	—
Felling		—	—	—	—	—	—	—	—	—	—	—
Coppicing		—	—	—						—	—	—

1. Ground preparation by ploughing, etc., is confined to times when the soil is workable and will not be damaged by machinery. On heavy clay soils the workable 'window' will be short, on wet peats, ploughing can be done at any time of the year.

2. Planting – any winter month except when the ground is frozen. The planting season can be extended by using cold stored plants or container grown plants.

3. Weeding (see Section 5.1). Glyphosate application is more effective on heavy weed growth if applied early in the season, i.e. May – June. Some conifers can be oversprayed with low doses of glyphosate in late summer after buds have set and foliage has hardened. The weather can seriously affect the time of herbicide application as most herbicide sprays require half a day of dry weather following application for the herbicide to work. Propyzamide requires a period of cold weather to be effective which may limit its use in spring.

4. Dotted lines indicate that the operation is marginal at this time and this will vary according to region.

Section 6
Landscaping and Conservation

Section 6   Landscaping and Conservation

Creating woodland on agricultural land constitutes a major change in land use pattern, the appearance of the landscape, and wildlife habitats. Depending on how planting is carried out there are many opportunities for enhancing both the landscape and wildlife values of the farm. The following sections give some guidance on how to achieve good design and improved habitat value. More detailed guidance on these aspects is provided in the companion volume to this Bulletin, *Farm woodland practice* and also in *The forestry and woodland code* published by TGUK, and *Conservation guidelines* published by the Department of Agriculture in Northern Ireland.

6.1 Landscape Design of Woodlands in Agricultural Areas

Planting new woodlands on farm land changes land use patterns and the appearance of the landscape. The new woods can look out of place, or they can blend with and enhance the landscape. The latter should be the aim. This section outlines the main points to consider when designing farm woodlands.

When planning new farm woodlands the first thing to consider is the existing landscape character of the area. This is important because different landscape types require different treatments. The main features to look at are the landform, existing vegetation patterns (especially semi-natural vegetation) land use patterns (in particular the prominence of hedgerows and hedgerow tree patterns), and the scale of the landscape (for instance whether the landscape is wide and rolling, or small and enclosed, as in a narrow valley).

These key points which farmers should take into account before planning and planting a new farm wood can be summarised in practical terms as follows.

1. Decide whether the landform is a more important feature in the landscape than an enclosure pattern of hedges and trees. This is easy if the landscape is open and treeless or has a strong pattern, but less so in other places.

2. If the landscape is mainly open and upland in character then the woodland or blocks of woodland should be irregularly shaped to follow landform, with the outside edges falling on spurs and rising into hollows. Geometric blocks following field patterns are unacceptable because the darker colour, coarser texture and height of the trees have a much greater impact than different coloured fields.

3. If the pattern of hedgerows is dominant in the landscape then smaller sized blocks and a more geometric layout is acceptable; in case of doubt, landform should be followed as above.

4. Even in lowland areas, the use of geometric shapes, for example in laying out species boundaries or rides within the wood, should be avoided.

5. Examine previous patterns of tree planting in the area and if attractive seek to develop them. Often the planting of knolls and low hill ridges enhances the landscape.

6. In most landscapes large woods or a series of medium sized woods linked by tall hedgerows have a more pleasing appearance than the patchy effect created by small isolated woodlands.

7. Consider views out from the farm, particularly from public places such as roads and footpaths, and try to frame views rather than block them.

8. The edges of small woodlands should be planted in such a way as to avoid a vertical face of conifers. By planting irregularly sized and spaced groups of broadleaves along the edge a much more natural effect can be created.

9. Planting can be used to screen unsightly artefacts or large farm buildings, thereby enhancing the landscape and helping new sheds and barns to sit more comfortably in the countryside.

10. Space should be left around any existing trees to allow them light and freedom to continue growing.

11. A large number of different tree species in a small conifer wood can look out of place, while a good selection of broadleaves is all right. Broadleaves rather than conifers should be used near to streams.

12. More complicated woodland shapes are likely to involve some increase in fencing costs. However, it is not necessary to follow a curved edge with a fence. Fencing in a series of straight lines with a little unplanted ground between fence and woodland edge is quite acceptable.

13. Treeshelters are useful for quick establishment, but they can be an eyesore. Olive green or brown shelters which blend with vegetation are better than white or bright green ones.

14. Professional advice on landscape design can be obtained and the Landscape Institute issues a register of landscape practices which will undertake this type of work (see Appendix C).

6.2 The Implications for Wildlife

When land is converted into woodland, the wildlife on that land is transformed. Most of the species present in pasture, meadows or arable fields are eventually replaced by woodland inhabiting species. The departure of grassland species, takes place mainly in the first 10–20 years after planting. The young trees grow together and kill the pre-existing vegetation by shading. Some woodland species move in during this early phase, but most have to wait 50 years or more until the woodland becomes more mature. Ecologically, therefore, the change to woodland does not happen on the day the trees are planted. Rather, it starts on that day, but continues for decades.

The main questions to consider for wildlife are.

1. Which are the sites which should, or should not, be planted?
2. How can species which are already present on the site in the grassland be maintained?
3. How can a wood with the capacity to become rich in wildlife be created?

Planting sites

From a wildlife point of view, new woodland should be established on land which has been used as arable or rotational grass, i.e. the type of land upon which the Farm Woodland Scheme is focused. Such land would be of little value for conservation in its existing state and the new woodland should be a considerable improvement.

The following types of land have a considerable existing wildlife value and this wildlife value would probably be lost if the land was planted.

1. Rough grazing.
2. Old grassland, which has not been ploughed for the last 10 years; not had herbicide broadcast in the last 5 years; has not been regularly dressed with fertiliser or slurry; and which contains a variety of non-grass species (including rushes and sedges). Such unimproved grasslands are rich wildlife habitats, but they have become very rare, and wherever possible examples should be preserved. This type of grassland is excluded from planting under the Farm Woodland Scheme except on a limited basis in the uplands.
3. Land used regularly for breeding by waders (e.g. curlew, redshank, snipe) and wintering wildfowl.

Keeping existing features

Even on land which is planted, there may be features of importance which are worth keeping.

1. *Hedges*
These will shelter a new plantation, and will help young trees to grow. Woodland wildlife will already be present in them, so keeping the hedges will enable woodland species to colonise the new woodland rapidly. Avoid planting right up to the hedge.
2. *Ponds and wet patches*
These are best retained by not planting right up to their margins. They should certainly not be drained. Keep taller trees to the north and east sides: this will enable the sun to beam in from the south and west. If natural scrub grows up beside the pond, allow some of it to develop.
3. *Grassland*
Where possible leave herb rich grassland unplanted. Include rides and glades in the design of the new plantation, placing them where the attractive species now grow. This will provide the best chance for attractive species to survive within the developing plantation.

Designing a wildlife-rich wood

Woods can eventually be made wildlife-rich by careful attention to design and choice of species at the outset. Much depends on the individual characteristics of the site, and the skill of the planter. Many features of woodland design are important for wildlife.

1. *Large size (say 5 ha or more)*
Larger woods tend to contain more habitats, in addition to shaded areas under the canopy, such as rides and glades and therefore attract more species.
2. *Rides and glades*
These open patches and access routes add greatly to habitat diversity. The edge between trees and open areas is usually good for wildlife, especially if it is irregular. These open areas will eventually be used for access, timber storage and machinery turning areas.
3. *Native tree species*
These are generally richer in wildlife than are exotic species, so if the main priority is conservation ideally planting should be restricted to native species. Choose the native species which are already present in the area.
4. *Native shrub species*
Many shrub species colonise new woods naturally, once the young trees are large enough to attract birds. However, it would be beneficial to help this process by planting some hazel, dog rose, or similar

native shrub species along margins and the edges of glades.

5. *Structural diversity*

If a mixture of tree species is planted, and planting is spread over a long period of time (10 years) then the differing canopy structures and ages produce a valuable habitat diversity. Allowing some natural scrub, and having areas of coppice also add to wildlife value.

6. *Wide spacing*

If the intended timber trees are planted at least 5 m apart, the spaces between may be colonised by natural scrub, and even saplings of valuable trees such as oak. This will add to the habitat diversity, and will be cheaper than high density planting. However, farmers should note the conditions on spacing laid down in the Woodland Grant Scheme, especially where they are planning to plant open ground which has previously been under agricultural production.

7. *Coppice*

This form of woodland management often generates rich wildlife habitats. New coppice areas should be placed beside rides and glades for maximum conservation benefit.

The management needs for conservation of existing woodland are different, especially in the case of ancient semi-natural woodland which is of high value for nature conservation. The requirements are summarised in a free booklet published by the Forestry Commission *Guidelines for the management of broadleaved woodland*.

References

FORESTRY COMMISSION (1985). *Guidelines for the management of broadleaved woodland*. Forestry Commission, Edinburgh.

McCURDY, R. J. (1987). *Conservation guidelines*. Department of Agriculture (NI) Forest Service, Belfast.

TIMBER GROWERS UNITED KINGDOM (1985). *The forestry and woodland code*. TGUK, London.

Section 7
Yields

Section 7 Yields

Wood yields are conventionally measured in terms of volume (cubic metres) although measurements may also be expressed in weight, for example for energy crops where the final product is chipped and yield is expressed in tonnes. Rates of growth are conventionally defined through yield classes as described below.

7.1 The Yield Class System

The Yield Class is a means of indicating the potential productivity of a stand of trees. The total volume production of timber of a stand up to any given age divided by the age of the stand gives a measure of average annual production, known as Mean Annual Increment (MAI). After planting, MAI increases with age, reaches a maximum and then declines. The growth rate of a crop with a maximum MAI of 20 cubic metres per hectare per year is defined as yield class 20. Faster growing stands, that is those of higher yield classes, will reach their maximum rates of growth earlier than slower growing stands. The volume measured in a standing crop is that of stemwood, defined as wood over 7 cm diameter, or in the case of broadleaves, the point in the crown where the trunk is no longer visible.

7.2 Assessment of Yield Class

To assess the yield class of a given crop it is necessary to establish the height of the stand and its age; the yield class is then read directly from a height/age curve. The height is that measured on the 100 largest (by diameter) trees per hectare. As examples of these models top height/age curves for sycamore and Japanese larch are shown in Figure 7.1.

7.3 Yield Models

The Forestry Commission has published nearly 1000 yield models for the major commercial tree species in Britain (Forestry Commission Booklet 48). Each model is a tabular presentation of stand growth and yield. The models cover a wide variety of spacing and thinning treatments. They can be used to compare the results of alternative treatments before deciding how to manage a stand or group of stands, and to forecast future thinning and felling yields.

Note that volumes derived from yield models do not include branchwood, which for broadleaved trees can form a significant quantity of the total saleable volume, especially where there is strong demand for firewood. For mature broadleaves, branchwood volumes may be 50 per cent of stemwood volumes (see Section 8 for values of branch wood).

7.4 Yields for Different Forestry Crop Systems

Conventional woodland (high forest)

Yields

The range of yield classes in Britain can be from as low as 4 for broadleaves to as high as 30 or more for some conifers. The yield class does not indicate when timber yields will be realised. This depends mainly on the thinning regime employed and the rotation length, which will vary depending on the owner's objectives.

Yields will vary depending on such factors as soil type, exposure, elevation and management treatment. Typical yields for slow growing broadleaves such as oak and beech are in the range yield class 4 to 8, faster growing broadleaves such as sycamore and cherry yield class 6 to 10, and poplar higher. Among the conifers, pines are usually lower, yield class 6 to 16, while spruces are yield class 10 to 24. For bare ground, particularly on sites which have carried an agricultural crop for some years, it may be very difficult to estimate the yield class with any reliability. The growth of tree stands on adjacent land may provide useful guidance, otherwise advice on yields for particular sites should be sought from local woodlands advisers.

Plant spacing

The advantages of wide spacing compared to close spacing are:

● reduced cost of cultivation, plants and planting;
● increases in individual size of trees.

The disadvantages of wide spacing are:

● losses of plants may cause large gaps;

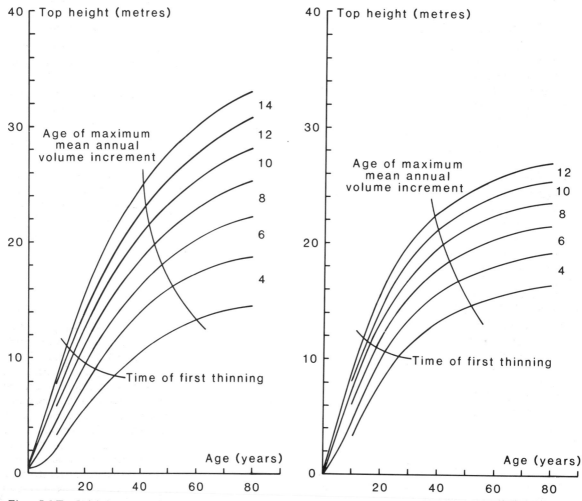

Figure 7.1 Top/height/age curves for (a) Japanese larch and (b) sycamore.

- canopy closure and thus full site utilisation takes longer to achieve and results in a loss of volume production;
- branch suppression is delayed, leading to larger knots and reduced timber quality;
- more rapid diameter growth results in wider annual rings and greater taper with a consequent reduction in sawn wood recovery;
- a smaller number of trees allows less choice in selecting good quality stems during thinning.

The choice of spacing to adopt must be a matter of judgement on the part of the manager after taking these factors into account for the site and crop.

Commonly used spacings for conifers are between 2 and 3 m. For broadleaves spacings are usually about

2 m except where there is existing woody growth to help draw up the young trees. For both broadleaves and conifers, wide spacing between trees leads to poorer choice for the final crop and usually poorer form, especially when planting grassy areas or other open land.

To calculate the number of plants per hectare for a particular initial spacing the following formula may be used:

$$\frac{(100)^2}{S} \text{ where S is the plant spacing in metres.}$$

Thus 2 metre spacing results in:

$$\frac{(100)^2}{2} = 50^2 = 2500 \text{ plants per hectare.}$$

64

Thinning

PURE STANDS

Thinning is the removal of trees from a stand during the course of the rotation. It is usually carried out in order to concentrate growth on the best formed trees, to improve stand quality by removing poorly formed and defective trees, to provide more growing space for the remaining trees so enhancing their diameter increment, and to generate intermediate revenue from a stand (although for early thinnings of small trees the operation may not always be profitable).

The most common type of thinning is known as selective thinning in which most of the suppressed and smaller trees are removed and groups of competing larger trees are broken up to encourage the development of the better trees and to leave a more open and uniform stand. Alternatively a systematic form of thinning (line thinning) taking out one line in every three or four may be used especially at the first thinning. On sites where the risk of windthrow is high, such as in the exposed uplands or where soil types restrict rooting depth, the serious danger of windthrow following thinning operations may lead to a decision not to thin crops. Light thinning maximises production per hectare but growth of individual trees is slower. Heavy thinning enhances individual tree growth at the expense of some loss of total volume production.

Thinning usually begins in conifers at about ages 20 to 35 (earlier for larch), and for broadleaves at about ages 25 to 40. However, these first thinning ages relate to traditional forestry and it is recognised that farmers will be able to harvest useful thinnings material such as stakes even earlier, especially from crops of species such as larch. Generally intervals between thinnings are 5 to 7 years in young stands, 8 to 10 years in middle aged stands and up to 15 years in older stands. These thinning intervals may be shortened especially in intensively managed farm woods. In general, the more vigorous the stand the shorter the cycle. The longer the interval between thinnings the greater will be the volume of produce harvested on each occasion; this has definite economic advantages. Typically farmers can expect thinning to yield 40 to 45 per cent of total production from their woods. The timing and size of trees taken out are heavily influenced by the thinning regime, although over a wide range of thinning regimes there is no effect on total volume production.

For broadleaved species the primary objective of thinning is usually to select for quality leaving the best stems to grow on. Thinning should aim to produce well-balanced, even crowns on final crop trees and defective, mis-shapen and vigorous (wolf) trees must be removed at an early stage. As there are usually few trees of good form the early selection of potential final crop trees may be a useful aid to thinning. Particular points to note when thinning broadleaves are:

1. light demanders such as ash and oak require more open stand conditions than sycamore and beech;
2. in many species heavy thinning may depress height growth and encourage the development of spreading, heavily branched crowns;
3. especially in oak and poplar, heavier thinnings may encourage epicormic branching.

Except in mixtures and for first thinnings of very dense plantations, systematic thinning methods such as the removal of one in four rows, generally have no place in thinning broadleaves. However, racks are necessary to minimise extraction damage throughout the rotation and these have to be laid out on the systematic pattern.

MIXTURES

Faster growing species, especially conifers, are often planted in mixtures with broadleaved species which are slow to establish, such as oak and beech. This is often done so that the faster growing species can act as a nurse crop; but also has the advantage of increasing yields and bringing early financial returns. The greatest difficulty in growing mixtures is to ensure that the final crop is not swamped by the supplementary species. Cleaning and frequent thinning at the right time will prevent this from happening, but may be expensive as the yields will be small. Regular thinning of mixtures is essential if the final crop species grows more slowly than other species in the stand as commonly happens in broadleaved/conifer mixtures. Neglect or delay in thinning is more serious in mixtures than in pure stands.

OLD NEGLECTED STANDS

The ability to respond to thinning may be reduced in old neglected stands. Opening up an old stand may increase the risk of windthrow and in broadleaves may cause dieback in the crown of the tree, development of epicormic branches, sun scorch or even stand collapse, for example in very old stands of beech. As a result, usually no more than 5–10 per cent of the trees should be removed in thinning at intervals of 10 years or more. Thinning must be selective to remove dead, dying and diseased trees.

Table 7.1 Yields for unthinned stands of poplar
YC 14   4.6 m spacing

Age yrs	Top height	Trees /ha	Mean dbh	B/A /ha	Mean vol	Vol /ha	Per cent mortality	MAI Vol/ha	Age yrs
7	11.8	470	16	9	0.09	40	0	5.7	7
12	18.5	465	24	21	0.30	139	0	11.5	12
17	24.2	449	30	33	0.60	272	0	16.0	17
22	28.8	439	36	45	0.97	426	0	19.4	22
27	32.4	431	40	55	1.32	571	0	21.1	27
32	35.1	425	44	64	1.64	696	0	21.7	32
37	37.2	420	46	71	1.89	794	0	21.4	37
42	38.7	416	48	76	2.09	868	0	20.7	42
47	39.8	412	50	80	2.24	924	0	19.7	47
52	40.6	409	51	83	2.37	969	0	18.6	52
57	41.3	406	52	85	2.47	1003	0	17.6	57

YC 14   7.3 m spacing

Age yrs	Top height	Trees /ha	Mean dbh	B/A /ha	Mean vol	Vol /ha	Per cent mortality	MAI Vol/ha	Age yrs
7	11.8	185	17	4	0.11	21	0	3.0	7
12	18.5	185	27	11	0.43	79	0	6.6	12
17	24.2	185	36	19	0.89	164	0	9.7	17
22	28.8	185	43	27	1.42	263	0	11.9	22
27	32.4	185	49	35	1.95	360	0	13.3	27
32	35.1	185	53	41	2.41	447	0	14.0	32
37	37.2	185	56	46	2.80	518	0	14.0	37
42	38.7	185	59	50	3.11	576	0	13.7	42
47	39.8	185	61	53	3.36	621	0	13.2	47
52	40.6	185	62	56	3.54	656	0	12.6	52
57	41.3	185	63	58	3.68	682	0	12.0	57

Widely spaced woodland

Agroforestry

Trees in agroforestry plantations are widely spaced compared with conventional woodlands and as a result overall yields of timber are generally much less, although individual trees are larger. Yields will vary greatly depending on a range of factors including site, tree and crop species, and spacings.

Poplar

Poplar stands are usually grown pure at wide spacings and not thinned. Yield tables for unthinned stands of yield class 14 poplar planted at 4.6 and 7.3 metres are shown in Table 7.1.

Poplars dislike competition, both above and below ground and only attain their fastest growth rates and largest dimensions when grown as isolated trees or in small groups or single tree rows. At spacings of 7–8 metres trees may be expected to reach veneer log dimensions before the onset of competition. Fast growing trees begin to produce veneer size logs at 12–15 years of age. High yielding pulpwood crops (200–300 cubic metres per hectare) on rotations of 12–15 years (yield classes around 20) appear quite feasible, the highest yields being obtained with trees planted 2–4 m apart.

Decorative timbers

Quality considerations are paramount and yield considerations are relatively unimportant for growing decorative timbers. In many species encouragement of open growth to obtain fast diameter growth and well developed crowns may be desirable. This is usually achieved by planting at wide (6 to 8 m) initial spacings to avoid competition or where trees have been closely spaced at planting by thinning to favour suitable quality stems.

Hedgerow trees

Hedgerow trees are typically open grown throughout their life and thus form large crowns with relatively short stems. The volume of stemwood of hedgerow trees will usually be assessed on an individual basis as follows:

$$V = D^2 \times L \times 0.0000785$$

where V = volume in cubic metres
L = length of timber in metres
D = diameter at the mid point of its timber length in centimetres.

Coppice

Coppice

The growth of a coppice crop is quite different from a plantation. Coppice stools may produce very high numbers of stems per hectare (over 100 000) with very rapid canopy closure and early culmination of maximum mean annual increment. Coppice is rarely thinned. Rotation lengths depend on the desired size and quality of poles and are typically 10–30 years depending on species and site. Initial growth of a coppice shoot is very vigorous; oak may reach 1 m and ash, sycamore and sweet chestnut as much as 2 m in the first year. Yield data are not comprehensive; mean annual increments over a coppice rotation, in terms of dry wood per hectare per year to 5 cm diameter are typically 2 tonnes for sycamore, birch, lime, oak, alder and sweet chestnut. Poplar and willow may produce as much as 6 tonnes per hectare per year.

Sweet chestnut is the most important commercial coppice crop. A provisional yield table for sweet chestnut coppice is given in Table 7.2.

Table 7.2 Yield table for sweet chestnut coppice

Age (years)	Volume (m³/ha) to 7 cm overbark	Fresh weight (tonnes/ha) to 7 cm overbark
5	–	–
10	25	25
15	80	80
20	160	160
25	270	265
30	405	400

Coppice with standards

At the end of each coppice rotation mature standards are felled, intermediate aged ones thinned, and new ones planted or recruited from natural regeneration or by retaining coppice shoots to grow on to larger size. Oak is generally retained for 5–6 coppice cycles (100–130 years) and ash for 3–5 cycles (60–100 years).

Stored coppice

Generally yields from stored coppice do not differ greatly from planted crops, but the pattern of growth is different. Early growth is more vigorous than in a planted crop but this greater vigour diminishes and by 70–80 years the initial growth advantage is usually no longer evident. There is some evidence that growth is poorer in stored coppice stands of over 100 years.

Short rotation coppice

Yields from short rotation coppice forestry are expected to average about 12 tonnes dry matter/ha/year.

Section 8
The Harvesting and Marketing of Woodland Produce

Section 8 The Harvesting and Marketing of Woodland Produce

8.1 Product Selection and Marketing Strategy

Marketing strategy

Before committing himself to a woodland investment or making decisions on how woods should be managed a farmer should consider carefully the possible end uses of the timber he may grow.

Farmers who are already successful in tree crops generally recommend that one should aim up-market, producing specialist products for markets not supplied by the large forestry enterprises. The farmer should try to add as much value to his tree products as he can afford, by using existing labour and machinery resources which would otherwise be idle. (See also Section 10.1 Farm Diversification Scheme). Perhaps above all, he should avoid competing directly with the Forestry Commission and the main forest management companies who can market large volumes of undifferentiated products at low profit margins.

Since farms will seldom have large quantities of wood to sell, the individual farmer can be in a weak trading position and there is potentially great benefit to be gained in forming or joining a co-operative with neighbours in the same position, particularly if some of them already have experience in selling timber. In Britain there is currently no financial assistance for marketing wood nor any price support system such as there is for most food products. (There are, of course, grant supports for tree planting (see Section 10), but not for marketing). By forming a co-operative a group of farmers may be able to offer larger volumes or continuity of supply and so attract lower costs for harvesting and higher prices from a buyer.

The marketing strategy, and hence the whole style of woodland management adopted by farmers, should take account of the great difference of size between the farm woods and the country's major forest blocks run by the Forestry Commission and the private forest management companies. The large conifer forests of the uplands produce large quantities of material suitable for bulk markets such as sawmilling, pulp, paper and particle board manufacture. In these markets, the small supplier will always be at a disadvantage in terms of the volumes offered for sale or for transport. The prices for produce are fixed (usually at the factory gate), and do not offer any incentive for improving quality as a means of increasing the revenue to the farmer. These markets provide a 'price floor' but the farmer should aim to do better.

Fortunately farm woods will usually be on better land than has been available to the large afforestation schemes in recent decades and the farmer can use this advantage to produce timber for a wider variety of markets. The farmer should maintain the distinction and avoid direct competition with the large forestry growers. By aiming for high value products from high quality material, the farmer can take advantage of local specialised markets not supplied by the large forest growers.

Market identification

After strategy the next objective for farmers should be to identify markets currently available. In broad terms these will fall into the following categories.

Broadleaves
Quality logs	veneer
	planking quality
Specialist markets	sports goods
Small roundwood	fencing
	pulpwood/chipwood
	firewood

Conifers
Sawlogs
Small roundwood (as above)
Specialist markets

In addition to market research which the farmer can carry out himself using forestry jourals such as *Timber Trades Journal* or *Forestry and British Timber*, professional advice will be available and should be sought (see Appendix C).

Prices

Broadleaves

Broadleaved trees yield what are technically 'hardwoods' to the timber trade (although some, such as poplar, are soft). The kind of buyer who will be interested depends on the species of tree, its size, quality and the quantity offered for sale. Good quality broadleaved timber may be used for the manufacture of veneers or as sawnwood for furniture, for heavy constructional work or for other specialist uses, such as turnery, carving, sports goods or tool handles. Lower quality logs may be used for the production of mining timbers, for hardwood pulp manufacture, fencing or firewood.

Prices may vary widely. Walnut, sycamore, cherry, and oak are in demand for veneer production and large diameter logs, even as short as 2.2 m, if they are of good quality, may sell for £100 to £300 per cubic metre on the farm, and for more if delivered. Great care must be taken when felling such logs as the merchant will inspect and price these logs when cut. For general use, sawmillers require sound, straight logs more than 3.5 m long and may take a wide variety of species, e.g. oak, beech, ash, sycamore, sweet chestnut and cherry. Prices for cut logs, on the farm, may range from about £30 to £100 per cubic metre, occasionally more, depending on size and quality. The amount of sawn timber that can be cut from a log depends on the size, the diameter at the top, and perhaps most importantly the straightness. Large logs fetch higher prices but there is also a premium for straightness. Evenly grown ash suitable for tool handles and sports goods (the wood should be white or pale pink in colour, not brown which is associated with brittleness and lack of flexibility) has a good market and fetches good prices (£40 to £80 per cubic metre on the farm) provided that it can meet the exacting specifications.

Conifers

Conifers yield what the timber trade calls 'softwoods' (although confusingly some are strong and may be quite hard). Again, buyers and prices depend on the species, sizes, quality and quantities offered for sale. Top quality conifer timber is used for joinery and for building construction. Lower quality material is used for packaging and pallets, fencing and mining timber. Small diameter material is used for pulp production and particle board manufacture. Virtually all conifers can be sold as pulpwood and particle board (although very resinous species such as larch may present special difficulties) and for common sawing, but some species can also supply special markets.

Scots pine for transmission poles (straight, defect-free stems with tight specifications for length, diameter and taper).
Larch in large, knot-free logs for boat-building and

whisky vats, though this market is small, and smaller sizes and lower qualities for fence posts, gate rails and rustic work.
Douglas fir in large sizes for heavy constructional timbers, and railway sleepers.

Conifer sawlogs may sell on the farm for £20 to £50 per cubic metre. Boatskin larch and select Douglas fir logs might be expected to fetch the upper price; small sawlogs (14 to 22 cm top diameter) and logs for posts etc. might sell for the lower figure. NB: These prices are underbark.

Table 8.1 Forestry Commission price-size relationship for conifers at 1987/1988 prices

Average volume per tree (m³)	Price (£ per cubic metre)	
	England and Wales	Scotland
0.06	0.00	−1.07
0.07	1.61	0.00
0.08	2.90	1.07
0.09	4.09	1.83
0.10	5.05	2.69
0.11	5.97	3.87
0.12	6.88	4.84
0.13	7.75	5.59
0.14	8.61	6.35
0.15	9.25	6.94
0.16	10.11	7.53
0.17	10.71	7.96
0.18	11.30	8.39
0.19	11.94	8.93
0.20	12.59	9.47
0.30	17.76	13.77
0.40	21.74	16.57
0.50	25.08	19.26
0.60	28.20	21.74
0.70	30.89	23.89
0.80	33.37	25.51
0.90	34.44	26.69
1.00	35.20	27.12
1.10	35.63	27.45
1.20	35.95	27.66
1.30	36.17	27.88
1.40	36.38	28.09
1.50	36.49	28.20
1.60	36.60	28.31
1.70	36.70	28.41
1.80	36.81	28.52
1.90	36.92	28.63
2.00	37.03	28.74

A long-term indication of the prices which may be expected for coniferous timber is given in Table 8.1. This shows the price–size curve data calculated by the Forestry Commission from its standing sales over the period 1957 to 1985 (Mitlin, 1987). The larger the mean tree size the greater the price per cubic metre within certain limits. At the bottom end the price for small sized material is governed by the demand for small roundwood. Farmers may be able to do better by adding value on the farm and selling ready converted products such as fence rails and prepared stakes.

The price for larger material improves in relation to its suitability for sawmilling. The price–size curve flattens off because most British sawmills are geared up to handle logs of up to 1 m³ average size. However, as indicated, high quality timber such as good Douglas fir and boatskin quality larch continues to rise in value.

While the price–size curves provide a valid indication of long-term expectation for conifers, in the short term farmers should use whatever indications they can obtain from recent local sales. An indication of current market prices for conifers can be obtained by referring to the forestry press. Summaries of all Forestry Commission conifer sales are published periodically in for example *Forestry and British Timber*.

A more generalised guide to current prices by the type of product for which the timber is suitable is given in Tables 8.2 and 8.3. These cover broadleaves and conifers.

Table 8.2 Approximate current prices for broadleaves

These will vary widely according to quality, distance from markets and the state of the supply and demand balance.

	Roadside	Delivered
Small roundwood and cordwood		
Fuelwood		
Pulpwood	£12–30	£15–35
Posts, stakes and rails	per tonne	per tonne
Low quality sawlogs		
Mining timber	£20–40/m³	£25–45/m³
Pallet, fencing and packaging		
Planking quality sawlogs		
Construction timber	£30–80/m³	£35–85/m³
Joinery timber and sawn boards		
Veneer quality logs	£80–300/m³	£90–320/m³

Table 8.3 Approximate current prices for conifers

These will vary widely according to quality, distance from markets and the state of the supply and demand balance.

	Roadside	Delivered
Small roundwood		
Posts, stakes, rails, pulpwood		
and chipwood	£12–25	£15–30
	per tonne	per tonne
Sawlogs		
Standard 18 cm td ub*	£30–50/m³	£32–60/m³
Merchantable 18 cm td ub	£25–40/m³	£27–50/m³
Merchantable 12 cm td ub	£20–35/m³	£22–45/m³
Shortlogs		
14 cm td ub	£18–35/m³	£20–45/m³

* Top diameter underbark in centimetres. Small roundwood is usually sold by overbark measurement or by weight, sawlogs by underbark measurement. Bark accounts for 10 to 15% of volume according to species and age.

Small diameter trees

Small diameter trees, both broadleaves and conifers, may be sold for manufacture into pulp or particle board (chipboard), though it should be noted that each mill is restricted by its technology to a range of species, and sometimes to a single species. Prices differ around the country, and within the catchment of each mill, with distance from the mill gate. Typically current prices are about £15 to £20 a tonne (approximately 1 cubic metre) up to 50 miles from the mill, from which transport must be deducted as well as the harvesting costs in order to calculate the 'gross margin' or surplus; the prices offered rise at greater distances from the mills to offset the higher transport costs.

Specialist product markets offer real advantage to farmers and should be sought by them if labour allows, since it is these which the large growers can seldom cater for. In various parts of the country turnery wood, pea stakes, bean rods, rustic wood, hop poles, carving woods, scout poles, etc., are all marketed and frequently at prices far in excess of those for sawlogs or even veneers. However, this refects markets where demand currently exceeds supply. If more material is produced then prices could fall.

Firewood

Farmers should not neglect the possibilities of marketing firewood. In many parts of the country this market pays more than the sale of wood to pulpwood, and the work of preparation has the special attraction that it is easily undertaken by the farm staff with simple equipment. Up to half of the total volume of large open grown broadleaves may be in the form of branchwood for which firewood forms a useful market. Supplying the farm itself with firewood may be financially attractive by substituting for other sources of energy.

Firewood could be sold at a farm shop or a 'collect your own scheme' could be developed to clear waste after harvesting. Most farmers with woodlands may decide to compromise by working small produce themselves with modified farm tractors (assuming there is some spare home labour and machine capacity) and either engage a contractor to handle large trees or sell them standing to a specialist timber merchant.

Timber sold for firewood provides a good example of the farmer's ability to add value. Sold standing in the wood firewood quality timber may fetch around £10 per tonne or per cubic metre. Cut to length and delivered it sells for £25 to £30 per tonne, or cut to length and sold by the bag at farm shop it sells for £1 to £1.50 per bag which often represents closer to £50 to £60 per tonne.

Poplar

At the present time poplar is selling well for pallet timber. Prices are similar to those for small to medium sized conifer logs at £25 to £30 per cubic metre at rideside.

Thus as an indication of likely income, a plantation of poplar growing at yield class 14 (see Section 7) felled at 35 years would produce around 480 m³/ha of logs with a top diameter under bark of 18 cm. This should yield £12,000 to £14,500 per hectacre after the 35 year rotation.

Cricket bat willow

Usually grown on 15 to 20 year rotation and trunks are sold by the 'roll', each roll being 2ft 4 ins (0.71 m) in length.

Price per roll varies with the girth of the tree as measured at 4ft 8 ins (1.42 m) above ground level as follows:

inches girth	cm dia	price per roll	price per m³
52–56	42–45	£16	£158–£123
57–61	46–49	£18	£138–£120
62–66	50–53	£20	£125–£111

With trees planted at 15 m spacings (45 trees per hectare) gross yield would be around £2,500 to £3,000 per hectare on a 15 to 20 year rotation.

Coppice

Sales from coppice fall into two categories. In Kent and Sussex, which are now the main coppice growing areas in England, sale of sweet chestnut coppice is well organised and may be by Private Tender, Private Treaty or Public Auction. Sweet chestnut coppice is usually sold standing with the cants (cutting areas) ranging from 0.5 to 2.0 hectares.

Recent (1987) prices achieved for sweet chestnut coppice have been as shown in Table 8.4.

Table 8.4 Prices achieved for sweet chestnut coppice in 1987

Cant size (ha)	Prices paid at auction £/ha		
	average	lowest	highest
less than 0.4	929	272	3,106
0.41–0.8	978	593	1,878
0.81–1.2	971	346	2,520
1.21–1.6	1,584	741	2,619
1.61–2.0	1,206	741	1,829
more than 2.0	1,077	494	2,520

These prices are rather depressed compared with the previous year and this is probably related to the October 1987 windblow in South East England.

Source: Strutt and Parker, Canterbury.

Outside south-east England markets are more opportunist with pole sized material being sold for pulp, chipwood, stakes and firewood as indicated above for small diameter trees.

For even smaller sizes specialist markets are available as discussed on page 73 and farmers taking advantage of slack time in the farm enterprise may be in a better position to exploit these than larger forestry organisations. A general guide to coppice yield and income is given in Table 8.5.

Short rotation coppice

As indicated in Section 2 this system is still very much in the development stages. Little of this material has been available up to now and as a result no market price structure has developed. The most useful comparisons which can be made are in relation to its use as an alternative fuel source. Early indications are that one or two hectares of this system should be able to generate sufficient fuel to keep an average sized three bedroom farmhouse heated on a continuing basis.

Table 8.5 Coppice yield and income

	Sweet chestnut	Oak	Ash, sycamore, other hardwoods and mixed coppice	Hazel
Rotation (years)	12−16	20−35	20−25	6−9
Yield (m³/ha/year)	5−8	3−7	6−10	3−5
Income* (£/ha)	650−2700	50−550	50−530	60
Markets	Stakes	Fuelwood	Fuelwood	Thatching
	Fencing	Charcoal	Pulpwood	Spars
	Hop poles	Fencing	Turnery	Hurdles

* assumes standing sales, so no harvesting costs incurred.

Table 8.6 Income from Christmas trees − based on £0.50/ft (£1.64/m)⋆

	Good forecast					
Tree size	3 ft (0.91 m)	4 ft (1.22 m)	5 ft (1.52 m)	6 ft (1.83 m)	7 ft (2.13 m)	Total
Year 5	(800) £1200	(400) £800	(400) £1,000			£3,000
6		(800) £1,600	(800) £2,000	(800) £2,400		£6,000
7			(800) £2,000	(800) £2,400	(800) £2,800	£7,200

	Poor forecast					
Tree size	3ft (0.91 m)	4ft (1.22 m)	5ft (1.52 m)	6ft (1.83 m)	7ft (2.13 m)	Total
Year 5	(615) £922	(615) £1,230				£2,152
6		(615) £1,230	(615) £1,537	(615) £1,845		£4,642
7			(615) £1,537	(615) £1,845	(615) £2,152	£5,535

The number of trees is given in parenthesis.
* Christmas trees are normally priced by their cut length in feet

Christmas trees and other produce

Norway spruce and some other conifers may be marketed seasonally as Christmas trees. At present Norway spruce is the most popular species for this trade in Britain, others are being developed at higher prices, especially noble fir and Scots pine which have attractive grey-blue colours and the graceful lodgepole pine which has bright green foliage. These species also offer the great advantage to the householder of having better needle retention.

Wholesale prices of Norway spruce for Christmas trees may be around 40p to 60p per foot (£1.31 to £1.97 per metre) of height (retail prices in suitable areas are roughly double) and about £1 or over per foot (£3.28 per metre) for blue firs. Prices are very market and quality dependent and these prices are a guide to the current situation which may change rapidly with an increase in supply.

An indication of the range and timing of income likely to be derived from Christmas tree production is given in Table 8.6. The figures in Table 8.6 have also been used to produce the cash flows shown in Appendix D, Table D7.

Some trees have foliage that is saleable; for example silver firs, western red cedar and Lawson cypress. There is a market for such greenery in Britain for wreaths but also an export market to Germany and some neighbouring countries for cemetery decoration, although the trade is not well developed.

Table 8.7 Advantages and disadvantages of harvesting by the farmer or contractor

Harvesting by the farmer

Advantages	Disadvantages
The farmer who has available labour and equipment reduces costs by felling the wood. He may also be able to prepare the timber further for example, by cutting to firewood, or by producing finished stakes and so increase the revenue. (See Section 12 on Training and Safety Requirements.)	Harvesting timber is dangerous work for inexperienced and untrained people: the larger the trees, the higher the risk of accidents. Newly blown trees and trees tangled by wind are the most dangerous.
The farmer himself has full control over access to the land and is in the best position to co-ordinate woodland work with other farm work (crossing fields in stubble, avoiding disturbance at lambing, minimising fence damage, etc.); that is difficult to achieve with contractors.	The existing standard tractor on the farm may not be effective for harvesting wood and a substantial investment may be needed to make it really suitable (e.g. a winch, wood-trailer, sub-frames, guards). The farmer should consider whether the volume of work would justify the expense.
Small volumes can be harvested by farm labour that would not interest a contractor.	High quality trees may be spoiled and seriously reduced in value by unskilled cutting.
By working the timber himself the farmer avoids all the potential problems of 'rogue' contractors and builds up his knowledge of values and how to grow material on his own farm for good market results.	Workers must be provided with suitable safety clothing and equipment.
	If harvesting is carried out over a long period timber may start to deteriorate.
	Haulage and marketing of small volumes are difficult.

Harvesting by contractor

Advantages	Disadvantages
The contractor should have experience and equipment to allow the harvesting operation to be done effectively and safely.	The contractor has to be paid from the sales revenue, and hence the profit to the farmer will be less.
The farmer does not have to invest in machinery or accessories that will be used only infrequently.	The possibility of supplying really specialist markets may be reduced.
The good contractor should be familiar with the log sizes in general market demand and should be able to cut the crop to maximise the revenue.	The care taken by a contractor (in transporting wood over arable or pasture, and in avoiding potential damage to ditches, fences, standing trees) is likely to be less than that taken by the farmer on his own land.
A co-operative may be able to offer the contractor a programme of work and negotiate a better price.	The farmer still has a responsibility for safety at work even though his timber is being cut by someone else: contracting does not avoid obligations for safe working practices on the farm (see Section 12).
Contractors may have secure markets for lower quality material such as small roundwood.	Some preparation of an area will be needed prior to a contractor starting and once he is working supervision will be required.

Harvesting/sales strategy

It is important to consider carefully whether the farmer himself should harvest the wood in his farm woodlands or whether he should sell it standing to a timber merchant or have it worked by a contractor.

Timing

Coppice is best cut in the autumn or early winter, when the sap is down and the trees are leafless. It is well to remember that timber is not a seasonal crop and, other than the considerations of access across arable fields or ley pastures, harvesting can take place at any time of year. The farmer should properly investigate the alternatives before committing himself to disposing of the crop to the first buyer who comes along. If markets are depressed, it may be worth leaving a crop for a few years.

Market specifications

Logs and other products must be cut to the specification of the purchaser and the farmer must know what those requirements are if he is to sell timber effectively, just as he would expect to know the market specifications for malting barley, seed potatoes or fat lambs if he should be selling those farm products. The contract may specify log lengths, minimum and maximum top and butt diameters and the tolerances of those. Species, straightness, presence of rot, splits or fluting: all these are among the features which may be specified, and failure to meet them may result in wood being rejected when it is delivered.

The specification of produce may have a considerable effect on the cost of harvesting and on the volume marketed from a particular area. For instance, a middle-sized conifer crop could be harvested for pulpwood. Virtually the whole crop could go into this market at a price of £20 a tonne at roadside, which with relatively low costs of cutting the trees and preparing the produce would give a surplus of around £10 a tonne. However, it would be financially advantageous to harvest and cut the same crop to supply several markets such as small sawlogs, posts and transmission poles, involving tight dimensional specifications, the removal of bark, careful debranching and high standards of selection for straightness; the tops and lower grade trees would then go to a less discriminating market, perhaps to particle board or to firewood depending on the respective prices. The values of the selected poles and sawlogs would be substantially higher than that of pulpwood in the alternative market strategy (sawlogs about £30 per cubic metre and transmission poles much more), but so also would be the costs of produce preparation. The more products which are cut the more skill is needed from the cutters. Outputs fall and harvesting costs will rise. The extra management input and costs of entering the higher specification markets must be weighed against the attraction of higher sales prices. Usually only two products are cut from a crop, but three may be worthwhile if a good price is expected. However, it pays the small grower to serve the specialist markets and the local markets, and to add value on the farm.

Timber measurement

Measurement of timber is required for many purposes. The most obvious of these is the need to estimate timber quantities for sale, but measurement is also needed for other management purposes such as inventory and production forecasting.

A wide range of measurement procedures is available and these have been comprehensively described in the Forestry Commission Booklet 39 *Forest mensuration handbook*. This deals with general aspects of measurement including the costs and benefits of different measurement procedures as well as describing in detail a range of procedures for the measurement of standing timber, felled timber, measurement by weight and stacked measure. A summarised version of the *Forest mensuration handbook*, designed for field use is available as Forestry Commission Booklet 49 *Timber measurement – a field guide*. Detailed advice on timber measurement is available from the Mensuration Branch of the Forestry Commission's Research Division at Alice Holt Lodge, Farnham, Surrey, GU10 4LH.

Traditionally, timber measurements are expressed in terms of solid volume, but other measures such as weight, stacked volume and number of pieces may be used. Measurements are conventionally expressed in metric units although the market for broadleaved timber largely retains the use of the hoppus system of measurement based on imperial units.

Contracts

Sale of timber is a fairly specialised subject and one which contains many potential pitfalls for the farmer. This is one aspect of farm woodland management where the inexperienced farmer may most benefit by seeking professional advice or help. Above all the farmer must insist on contract terms being properly specified. As a guide to the contract terms, which it is often prudent for the farmer to include, an outline contract for the sale of timber is included as Appendix F.

8.2 Price Trends and Inflation

The price of timber has fluctuated widely over the last decade which makes comparison with other prices, and future predictions, very difficult. Taken in the long term over most of the period 1900 until the present day, however, prices have shown a broadly consistent upward trend showing an average real (i.e. above inflation) growth of 1–2 per cent per year (Johnson *et al.*, 1967). Predictions have been made of future real price increases of between one-half per

Table 8.8 Long-run price indices

Imported sawn softwood real price index						Real price index for homegrown hardwood logs	
Year	Unit	Year	Unit	Year	Unit	Year	Unit
1870	27	1909	35	1948	77	1948	
1871	21	1910	35	1949	69	1949	
1872	21	1911	34	1950	67	1950	
1873	26	1912	33	1951	95	1951	
1874	30	1913	35	1952	91	1952	
1875	27	1914	35	1953	79	1953	
1876	28	1915	41	1954	79	1954	90
1877	29	1916	51	1955	84	1955	
1878	27	1917	57	1956	82	1956	
1879	24	1918	66	1957	78	1957	
1880	28	1919	50	1958	70	1958	77
1881	28	1920	44	1959	64	1959	69
1882	29	1921	39	1960	69	1960	64
1883	28	1922	38	1961	70	1961	72
1884	28	1923	41	1962	65	1962	73
1885	30	1924	37	1963	66	1963	73
1886	29	1925	36	1964	69	1964	74
1887	29	1926	36	1965	71	1965	76
1888	30	1927	38	1966	69	1966	77
1889	33	1928	38	1967	66	1967	79
1890	31	1929	38	1968	70	1968	76
1891	28	1930	42	1969	74	1969	77
1892	31	1931	39	1970	75	1970	80
1893	30	1932	36	1971	71	1971	74
1894	33	1933	36	1972	68	1972	72
1895	32	1934	39	1973	92	1973	101
1896	34	1935	36	1974	123	1974	102
1897	36	1936	36	1975	93	1975	78
1898	35	1937	41	1976	97	1976	78
1899	34	1938	40	1977	98	1977	88
1900	36	1939	42	1978	82	1978	105
1901	35	1940	56	1979	79	1979	110
1902	35	1941	65	1980	100	1980	100
1903	36	1942	66	1981	80	1981	81
1904	35	1943	77	1982	81	1982	
1905	34	1944	80	1983	71	1983	
1906	34	1945	68	1984	72	1984	
1907	34	1946	71	1985	64	1985	
1908	35	1947	83				

Sources: Sawn softwood imports – *Timber Trades Journal, Centenary Supplement, 1973; FAO Yearbook of Forest Products 1985*. Home grown hardwood logs – *Wholesale Price Index of homegrown hardwood in the round and standing*. DTI, London.

cent per annum (US Forest Service, 1980) and 2½ per cent per annum (World Bank, 1979). Economic theory suggests that a commodity such as timber which is a well-established product, will be in balanced future supply and demand, which may involve moderate increases in the long term.

Table 8.8 shows the indices for the real price of imported sawn softwood from 1870 to 1985 and homegrown hardwood (broadleaved) log prices from 1958 to 1981. These two series give an indication of the long-term price stability of timber as a commodity.

It can be seen that timber prices fell rapidly in the early 1980s and are only just beginning to catch up with inflation. This followed a long and sustained bull market in the 1970s pushing timber up to record levels which have still not been regained. Prices in long and medium term contracts did not fall so much, and generally take much longer to reflect external shocks to the price mechanism. The moral of most of this is that in the short term, prices fluctuate rapidly and so current prices cannot be used as an indication of long-term prices. Prices in the long run (50 years or more usually) are what affect revenue, and so estimates of long-term prices should be used in appraising forest crops (see Mitlin, 1987).

The two measures of industry output prices indicate currently a healthy industry that is managing to keep prices in line with inflation. Indeed the paper industry is a large market for domestic timber and has just emerged from a particularly lean period in its history. There is always likely to be a market for domestically produced timber as, at the moment, Great Britain can only supply about 12 per cent of its needs, and it is unlikely that this figure will ever rise above 25 per cent. Buoyant markets, and the prospects of perpetual demand for domestic timber, make current price variations one of the smaller risks of investing in timber. It must always be remembered that, unlike most products, the timber grower can decide when to market the product to his best advantage, and so short-term fluctuations in price can always be avoided by leaving the trees in the ground.

Compared to agricultural product prices, timber has just started to out-perform these in terms of price growth. There are two reasons for this. Firstly, as has already been mentioned, timber prices have recovered in real terms over the last 5 years. Secondly, agricultural prices have not increased in real terms over the last 5 years by very much. This has led to an improvement in the relative price of timber to crop outputs, which will make timber investment look a more attractive use of farm land.

References

JOHNSTON, D.R, GRAYSON, A.J. and BRADLEY, R.T. (1967). *Forest planning*. Faber, London.

MITLIN, D.C. (1987). *Price-size curves for conifers*. Forestry Commission Bulletin 68. HMSO, London.

US FOREST SERVICE (1980). *An analysis of the timber situation in the United States, 1952–2030*. US Department of Agriculture, Washington DC.

WORLD BANK (1979). *Softwood prices: trends and outlook*. Commodity Note 15. IBRD, Washington DC.

Section 9
Returns from Woodland Investments

Section 9 Returns from Woodland Investments

9.1 Investment Appraisal

Investment appraisal is important as an aid to decision making both at the initial stage of planting trees and in their later management when considering such operations as cleaning, pruning and thinning. Further details on the application of investment appraisal to woodlands are given in Forestry Commission Booklet 47 *Investment appraisal in forestry* by Busby and Grayson.

Because of the long time periods involved in woodland management, investment appraisal calculations are done in real terms. This simply means that it is assumed that all future costs and revenues increase due to inflation by the same amount, so that inflation can be ignored. Remember, however, that because inflation is ignored the figures in an appraisal cannot be used for budgeting, unless inflation is taken into account when the budget is drawn up. It is also important to note that percentage figures used in an appraisal (such as the rate of return or interest rates) must also be real figures, and therefore be net of the rate of inflation.

There are two ways of expressing returns from an investment.

1. The profit or loss from the investment at a given interest rate.

2. The interest rate at which revenue exactly equals expenditure (thus showing the percentage return on that expenditure.

As the second is more difficult to calculate (although it may be more appealing as a measure of performance), concentration will centre on the first measure of returns.

Money that is invested in a project could have been used for something else. In the alternative uses, it would have earned some return or rate of interest. By putting it into a project that interest is lost or foregone in order to get the returns that the project has to offer. One way of deciding whether the returns from this project are higher than those in the alternatives is to calculate a discounted cash flow.

A discounted cash flow takes all the expenditures and revenues from the project over its entire life and expresses them as a profit or loss figure in year 0. What does this mean? Year 0 is now, but the revenues and expenditures are spread out over maybe the next 50 years. The way this problem is overcome is by discounting each figure to get its present (i.e. year 0) value.

Discounting is the opposite of compounding. It reduces the value of future sums of money or discounts them to take into account the assumed rate of interest (now called a discount rate) and the time at which they occur. It therefore enables alternative options to be ranked and can be used to compare profits or losses from the project, expressed in terms of present value (called Net Present Value or NPV).

Net Present Value is used in investment appraisal as it gives a value in present terms to different projects, taking into account the interest rate, all the expenditures and revenues, and the times at which they occur.

The Internal Rate of Return (or IRR) of a project is defined as the interest rate at which NPV = 0. Therefore it can be said that the project earns that particular rate of return. If NPV is greater than 0 then this suggests that the project is earning more than the rate of interest. If NPV is less than 0, however, this suggests the opposite, that the rate of return is less than the assumed interest rate. In other words taking on the project would incur a loss, as higher returns could be obtained by investing in an alternative.

With these techniques of evaluation in mind, tables have been constructed to make the arithmetic simpler. Suppose, for example, a farmer chooses a real discount rate of 6 per cent as being the most appropriate and is faced with the following cash flow from a woodland investment.

Year	Expenditure £	Revenue £
0	1,000	
1	300	
3	180	
7	200	
12	60	15
25		8,020
35		12,050

The discounted cash flow is constructed by multiplying each figure by the discount factor shown in Appendix G under the appropriate discount rate and at the correct point in time. Discounted revenue (DR) and expenditure (DE) can then be calculated and DE subtracted from DR then gives the NPV of the project.

Year	Discount factor	Expend-iture	DE	Revenue	DR
0	1.0000	£1,000	£1,000.00		
1	0.9434	£300	£283.02		
3	0.8396	£180	£151.13		
7	0.6651	£200	£133.02		
12	0.4970	£60	£29.82	£15	£7.46
25	0.2330			£8,020	£1,868.66
35	0.1301			£12,050	£1,567.70
			£1,596.99		£3,443.82

$$\text{Net present value} = \text{Total discounted revenue} - \text{Total discounted expenditure}$$
$$= £3,443.82 - £1,596.99$$

An easy way to think of discounting is to take a discounted figure, say the £151.13 expenditure in year 3. If £151.13 was saved in year 0, earning 6 per cent interest per annum, then by year 3 it would have grown to £180 which is exactly the amount required in that year. This should clarify the point that £151.13 in year 0 is exactly the same as £180 in year 3, except that the interest has not yet been added. It also follows from this that any compound factor in a year, at a given rate is:

$$\text{Compound factor} = \frac{1}{\text{Discount factor}}$$

since:

$$\text{Present value} = \text{future value} \times \text{discount factor}$$

therefore:

$$\frac{\text{Present value}}{\text{Discount factor}} = \text{compounded (future) value}$$

9.2 Project Life and its Effect on Returns

Net present value as described above can help the landowner decide whether a forest investment is beneficial or not. Either the rate of return can be calculated to compare with alternative rates of return (from other potential investments), or the NPV at a given or desired rate of return (i.e. the chosen discount rate) can be derived. One problem is, however, that when comparing NPVs of alternative projects, the length of the project becomes important. For example, one opportunity may yield an NPV of say £180 and another one only £150. If, however, the second project had a life only half that of the first, then it could be run twice to get an NPV of £150 plus an NPV at the beginning of the second project run of £150 (which would have to be discounted back itself to year 0). Obviously this is an extreme example, but a similar comparison could be made between projects with only slightly different lives (e.g. four 60-year projects could be run in the same time as three 80-year projects). Hence, some measure of NPV per year is necessary.

Net present value cannot merely be divided by the number of years in the project since it has already been shown that figures far into the future have a low present value. Hence, the annual figure derived has to be slightly larger to take into account the (average) effect of discounting these annual 'profits' over time. Appendix G Table G.2 gives suitable factors for performing this task. For example, an NPV of £580 from a project lasting 18 years, discounted at 11 per cent, would be equivalent to an average annual 'profit' of:

$$£580 \times 0.1298 = £75.28$$

The resultant values are called *annual equivalents* and can apply to discounted costs (annual equivalent cost), discounted revenues (annual equivalent revenue) and NPV (which is often just referred to as the annual equivalent). Two other uses can be made of such a table as well.

Writing off expenditure

A purchase of something expensive such as a tractor, forwarder or chipper may be paid off over several years with the aid of a bank loan. To estimate how much this might cost at current rates of interest (in this case it would be appropriate to use the APR, as we are now talking about budgeting rather than appraising) the figures in Appendix G Table G.2 can be used. For example, a tractor costing £45,000 could be written down over 6 years at 12 per cent interest at an annual cost of:

$$£45,000 \times 0.2432 = £10,944.$$

This could, of course, then be put in an appraisal as an annual rather than one-off cost, but care would have to be taken as confusion between real and nominal (i.e. monetary) values and interest rates may arise, and the effects of taxation would also complicate matters.

Recurring costs in an appraisal

Just as the table can transform present values into a stream of annual values, the reverse is also true. To get a present value factor for a stream of recurring figures, merely invert (or divide into one) the relevant factor in the table to get a figure that represents the 'present value of £1 per year'. For example, $1/0.1284 = 7.79$ is the present value of £1 per year over 9 years at a 3 per cent interest rate. This figure can then be used as a factor by which to multiply other annual amounts. For the given example, if an annual cost was £8, then the discounted cost of that would be:

$$£8.00 \times 7.79 = £62.31$$

If the stream does not start in year 1, then the relevant factor can be calculated as:

present value of £1 per year from year a to b

= present value of £1 per year from 1 to b

− present value of £1 per year from year 1 to $(a-1)$.

The latter two figures can easily be derived from the table. For example, if the £8.00 per year was not from year 1 to 9, but year 7 to 18, its present value could be calculated as:

$$(1/0.0727 - 1/0.1846) \times £8.00$$

$$= (13.76 - 5.42) \times £8.00$$

$$= (8.34) \times £8.00$$

$$= £66.72.$$

With these techniques it should now be possible to carry out fairly comprehensive appraisals of forest investments.

Reference

BUSBY, R. J. N. and GRAYSON, A. J. (1981). *Investment appraisal in forestry*. Forestry Commission Booklet 47. HMSO, London.

Section 10
Grants and Tax Arrangements

Section 10 Grants and Tax Arrangements

10.1 Grant Schemes

Farm Woodland Scheme

Conditions of the Scheme

1. Targeting: the scheme is confined mainly to areas formerly in arable use or grassland of less than 10 years age. The rationale for this is to increase savings on agricultural support (and to meet environmental concern over afforestation of the limited area of semi-natural land in the lowlands). To accommodate farmers in the hills an allocation of 3000 hectares of rough grazing in the Less Favoured Areas will be admitted over the 3 years of the scheme.
2. Rates of payment: annual payments are as follows.

Lowland	£190/ha
Less Favoured Areas	
Disadvantaged Area	£150/ha
Severely Disadvantaged Area	£100/ha
Rough grazing (DA or SDA)	£ 30/ha

The rates of annual payment have to be reviewed by Ministers no later than 30 September 1991 and periodically at intervals of no more than 5 years thereafter.

3. The area target for the scheme stands at 36 000 hectares over 3 years, following which the scheme is to be reviewed.
4. Period for annual payments.

Pure crops of oak and beech (up to 10% other broadleaves allowable)	40 years
Other pure broadleaved crops and mixtures containing more than 50% broadleaves	30 years
Pure conifers and mixtures containing less than 50% broadleaves	20 years
Coppice	10 years

Short rotation coppice (rotations less than 10 years) will not be eligible.

5. Area thresholds: a maximum of 40 hectares per holding everywhere. A minimum of 3 hectares per holding, one hectare per block (in Northern Ireland one hectare per holding).
6. Eligibility will be conditional upon acceptance into the Forestry Commission/Northern Ireland Forest Service Woodland Grant Scheme. The woodland will also have to form part of the applicant's farming operations, so afforestation of the whole holding or sale to a forestry investor would not qualify for annual payments.

Woodland Grant Scheme

Table 10.1 Rates of grant

Area approved for planting or regeneration (hectares)	Conifers £ per hectare	Conifers planted under the Farm Woodland Scheme £ per hectare	Broadleaves £ per hectare
Area band 0.25–0.9*	1005	630	1575
1.0–2.9	880	505	1375
3.0–9.9	795	420	1175
10 & over	615	240	975

* Band 1 covering areas of less than 1 hectare is not available to farmers under the Farm Woodland Scheme

It should be noted that where conifers are planted under the Farm Woodland Scheme a lower rate of grant applies.

For new planting on existing arable or improved grassland of less than 10 years of age which is undertaken outside the Farm Woodland Scheme, there will be a supplement of £200 per hectare.

Applications relating to the establishment and restocking of broadleaved woodland will be subject to the provisions of the *Guidelines for the management of broadleaved woodland* published by the Forestry Commission.

Full details of the Woodland Grant Scheme are set out in a free leaflet issued by the Forestry Commission/ Northern Ireland Forest Service which will be made available to all farmers enquiring about the Farm Woodland Scheme.

Grants are also available from a number of sources shown in Table 10.2.

Those from the Countryside Commission and the Nature Conservancy Council are discretionary and are generally related to the specific objectives of the agency concerned. They are based on a grant payment of a specific percentage of acceptable costs.

A number of grants are currently available on a wide range of capital investments from Agricultural Departments under the Agricultural Improvement Scheme. There are two basic schemes the AIS(EC) and the AIS(N), the European Commission and National Schemes respectively.

Grants under the AIS(EC) Scheme have been designed to meet the needs of agricultural businesses with an income per labour unit below the national average non-agricultural wage. The aim is to improve economic performance. Grant aid under the scheme has an overall limit in any 6 year rolling period of £35,000 per labour unit up to a general maximum of £50,000 per business whichever is the less. Grant payments will also depend on the eligibility of the claimant and the farm business. There is a minimum eligible expenditure of £1,500. To qualify for grant aid under the AIS(EC) Scheme the proposals must form part of an improvement plan approved by the relevant Agricultural Department before work commences. Subject to certain conditions an enhanced rate of grant may be available under this scheme for young farmers under 40 years of age.

The AIS(N) Scheme is designed to encourage capital investments by businesses which cannot or do not wish to carry out an improvement plan. The range of eligible activities is limited to 1. energy saving investments, 2. environmentally positive investments and 3. horticultural investments. In Scotland only arterial drainage and river works are included in the range of eligible activities. Prior approval except for arterial drainage work is not necessary. There are still, however, certain requirements regarding eligible persons and eligible businesses and the grant ceilings remain the same and must take into account expenditure under both the AIS(EC) and AIS(N) Schemes.

Under the AIS(N), expenditure on certain items including provision, replacement and improvement of hedges (including hedgerow trees), walls and dykes, where the walls and dykes are built of traditional local material and the provision, replacement and improvement of shelter belts including trees for shading stock plus orchard replacement or planting can be eligible for an enhanced ceiling up to a further £24,000 per business subject still, however, to the limit of £35,000 per labour unit. Subject to the requirements and limits of the schemes, grants are paid at the rate shown for the items listed.

Certain items under the AIS schemes of particular interest in this context are grant aidable at standard costs as opposed to actual costs. These costs are what it is estimated it would cost in labour and materials to do the work to a certain specification. Details of items and standard costs which change from time to time are available from the local Ministry or Departmental office.

In most cases, prior approval from the grant aiding body is necessary and in some cases consultation between various parties may be necessary before approval for the proposals can be given. These consultations and considerations inevitably take time. It is therefore essential that sufficient time should be allowed for these necessary preliminaries before the date work is due to start.

Grants under the Crofting Counties Agricultural Grants Scheme are also available but only to crofters, and occupiers of like status to crofters, in the crofting counties of Scotland.

It is obviously impossible to give all the details of these schemes in this publication and therefore if in doubt it is recommended that potential applicants consult the Agency, Ministry or Department concerned prior to beginning work or entering into any financial commitments. It should also be noted that as a general rule grant aid is not paid by more than one Agency, Ministry or Department for the same work and there are certain mutual exclusivity rules included in the AIS Scheme.

Farm Diversification Grant Scheme

Grants provided under this scheme, which came into operation on 1 January 1988, are intended to assist existing agricultural businesses to develop alternative commercial uses for agricultural buildings and land. The Scheme is designed to help farmers develop enterprises which are farm based but non-agricultural. It does not cover alternative crops or forestry but does include farm based industry, including the processing of timber, farm shops, pick your own facilities, accommodation and catering, sports and recreation, educational facilities which are farm and countryside orientated, livery and horses for hire, amongst other items. Grants for feasibility studies and initial marketing costs are expected to become available in the spring of 1988.

The basic grant rate is 25 per cent, except to young farmers, on a limit of £35,000 overall expenditure in any six-year period. Young farmers under 40 years of age who satisfy the conditions of the Scheme may be eligible for an additional premium bringing the grant rate up to 31.25 per cent.

The life of the plan may be from 1 to 6 years and prior approval of the plan is necessary before expenditure is incurred.

Further details of this Scheme are available at your local Ministry or Agriculture Department offices.

Set-Aside Scheme

Set-aside is a voluntary scheme designed to reduce surpluses of arable crops. In return for taking out of production at least 20 per cent of their land growing certain arable crops in the base year 1987/88, farmers receive annual compensation payments of up to £200 per hectare of land set aside. Those who wish to plant trees on set-aside land have a choice between:

first woodland option: direct set-aside to woodland, *or* second woodland option: set-aside through the Farm Woodland Scheme.

Under either option, approval must be obtained for planting the land concerned under the terms of the Forestry Commission's Woodland Grant Scheme. The only exceptions are listed below.

Areas of less than 0.25 of a hectare. These are not eligible for the Woodland Grant Scheme, but farmers may plant such areas without planting grants, or with other grants such as local authority or Countryside Commission amenity tree-planting grants. In these cases they would receive woodland set-aside rates of annual payment.

Planting of short-rotation coppice (for energy or biomass). This is not eligible for planting grants, but may be planted as a non-agricultural use with the appropriate rate of set-aside payment which reflects the earlier income that accrues from such coppicing.

Planting of fruit trees and orchards, Christmas trees or hardy nursery stock for sale, which are not permitted under the Set-Aside Scheme.

Direct set-aside to woodland

Grants are payable by the Forestry Commission for approved planting under the Woodland Grant Scheme. See Table 10.1 for current rates. The supplement of £200 for planting on better land under the Woodland Grant Scheme is not available. In addition to the planting grants, farmers will receive the woodland set-aside payments of £180 on land in less-favoured areas and £200 elsewhere. Payments will continue for the duration of the set-aside agreement only. If the farmer has not received approval from the Forestry Commission or not yet planted trees on the area concerned at the end of the year, he will be eligible for the permanent fallow rate of payment provided that the fallow conditions have been observed.

Set-aside through the Farm Woodland Scheme

The relevant planting grants under the Forestry Commission's Woodland Grant Scheme are also given in Table 10.1. The rates of annual payments are set out in paragraph 2 of the Farm Woodland Scheme entry earlier in this section of the Bulletin, together with the main conditions of the Farm Woodland Scheme which must be met. Farmers who wish to plant more than 40 hectares may apply for 40 hectares under the Farm Woodland Scheme option and the remainder under the first woodland option. If ineligible for the Farm Woodland Scheme or if it is oversubscribed in the year of application, the farmer may either consider woodland under the first woodland option or may leave the land fallow. Further details of the Set-Aside Scheme are available from Agriculture Department offices.

Environmentally Sensitive Area Schemes

Environmentally sensitive areas are areas of recognised importance from an ecological or landscape point of view. A number of schemes have been implemented or are proposed throughout the UK for areas where agricultural practices have created or are affecting the ecological or landscape interest. The details of each area scheme vary and the items for which payments may be made differ from scheme to scheme. Further information on these and the geographical boundaries of each scheme area are available at local Ministry or Agriculture Department offices.

It should be remembered that grant rates, grant ceilings and eligible items for all schemes may vary from time to time.

10.2 Consultation

In order to ensure that the requirements of land use, agriculture, amenity, recreation and nature conservation are taken into account before decisions are reached on grant aid, the Forestry Commission operates, under its grant scheme, a system of consultation with a range of statutory authorities. These are designed to reconcile any conflict of view that might arise between the applicant and such authorities. The Woodland Grant Scheme forms an integral part of the Farm Woodland Scheme, so that similar arrangements will apply. A system of thresholds agreed with authorities concerned ensures that in certain circumstances small or otherwise non-controversial proposals can be approved by the Forestry Commission without consultation, although there will still be liaison with Agriculture Departments in the case of Farm Woodland Scheme applications.

Where consultation is required, the Forestry Commission sends details of the proposals to the appropriate authority, seeking a response within 28 days. Where objections arise, the Commission tries to resolve these by discussion with all the parties involved with an overall period of two months from the start of the consultation process. When it is not possible to resolve objections, the applicant may choose to have the case referred to the Commission's appropriate Regional Advisory Committee to assist in trying to find a compromise solution acceptable to all the parties concerned. Regional Advisory Committees are appointed by the Forestry Commissioners for each of the Commission's Conservancies, and comprise a Chairman, four members representing forestry interests and four representing respectively the interests of agriculture, planning, the environment and the Trade Unions. Where the Regional Advisory Committee has not been successful in reconciling the parties and the applicant wishes his proposal to receive further consideration, the case is referred to the Forestry Commissioners.

Where, after taking account of the Regional Advisory Committee's discussions with the parties, the Commissioners agree with the other authorities consulted that an application or plan should be refused in whole or in part, they may give a decision on the application without reference to Ministers. In all other cases, the Commissioners are required before giving a decision to seek the views of the Ministers concerned.

In announcing the proposals for the Farm Woodland Scheme, the Government made clear that it was concerned to try and simplify the scheme as far as possible and to keep administrative costs to the minimum. To this end, it is intended to reduce the amount of consultation with local authorities on planting of farm woodlands where small areas are involved. Existing arrangements will continue in National Designated Areas such as SSSIs, Environmentally Sensitive Areas, National Parks and National Scenic Areas (Scotland).

10.3 Farm Woodland Taxation

Farm Woodland Scheme

Payments made to farmers under the Farm Woodland Scheme are made in lieu of farming income and are taxable in the same way as the agricultural income which they are intended to replace.

Commercial woodlands

Farm Woodlands within the Farm Woodland Scheme will usually be commercial woodlands, that is woodlands managed on a commercial basis and with a view to the realisation of profits. The Chancellor announced in his 1988 Budget speech that commercial woodlands were to be wholly removed from the scope of income tax and corporation tax. This means that expenditure for the cost of planting and maintaining the trees will not be allowed as a tax deduction against other income; and the proceeds from the sale of the trees will not be charged to tax. It follows that farmers who occupy these commercial woodlands will not be taxable either on the planting grant they receive in connection with these woodlands or the proceeds from the timber. Equally they will not be able to offset planting and other costs against their other income including farming profits.

Non-commercial woodlands

Farmers however may also occupy other woodlands which are not commercial woodlands. If these woodlands are held for amenity value then all receipts and expenses are outside the scope of income tax and this position has not changed. Where trees are neither commercial woodlands nor amenity woodlands but are ancillary to the farm business itself, e.g. if they are part of a hedgerow or shelterbelt, then the revenue expenditure and receipts from timber will form part of the normal farming expenses and should be reflected in the farming accounts. Capital expenditure on establishing a shelterbelt will normally qualify for Agricultural Buildings Allowance of 4 per cent per annum on a straight line basis.

Record keeping

As for any separate business activity separate records and accounts will be required. This will be particularly important for both commercial and amenity woodlands where expenses cannot be set off against farming income.

Capital Gains Tax

The effect of special rules applying to computation of gains and losses arising on the disposal of commercial woodlands is to exclude growing timber (as distinct from the land on which it stands) from assessment. In other words capital gains tax is charged only on the increase in value of the underlying land.

Inheritance Tax

Inheritance tax was introduced in the Finance Act 1986 to replace capital transfer tax. The tax applies to transfers on death and within 7 years of death and to certain other lifetime transfers. There is a specific deferment relief for transfers of woodlands on death which allows for an election to be made (normally within 2 years of death) to have the value of the standing timber (but not the land) left out of account in calculating the tax payable. If the beneficiary then disposes of the timber before his death, tax is charged on the sale proceeds or on the value of the timber at the time of the disposal. The taxable amount is treated as the top slice of the deceased's estate for the purpose of calculating the tax liability. If the timber is trans-ferred again on another death no tax is chargeable on subsequent disposals by reference to the first death. Woodlands may qualify for business property relief if they are run on a commercial basis or for agricultural property relief if occupation is ancillary to that of agricultural land. Both reliefs operate by reducing the value on which tax is charged by either 50 or 30 per cent depending on the nature of the interest in the property comprised in the transfer.

Where woodlands are accepted by the Board of Inland Revenue as of outstanding scenic, historic or scientific interest, or as essential for the protection of the character and amenities of a building of outstanding historic or architectural interest, inheritance tax and capital gains tax relief can be claimed, subject to suitable undertakings being given to conserve the qualifying interest.

VAT

Commercial woodland operations constitute a taxable supply (Schedule 6, VAT Act 1983), and registration is mandatory where turnover exceeds £7,000 in any quarter or £20,500 in any year.

Table 10.2 Summary of grants available

Eligible works	Forestry Commission and Northern Ireland Forest Service		Ministry of Agriculture, Fisheries and Food, Department of Agriculture and Fisheries for Scotland, Department of Agriculture Northern Ireland and Welsh Office Agriculture Department		Countryside Commission‡ Countryside Commission for Scotland‡		Nature Conservancy Council‡	
	Grant	Points	Grant	Points	Grant	Points	Grant	Points
Amenity tree planting (other than woodland management)	Nil		LFA 60% Other 30% LFA 30% Other 15%	Works eligible include the planting of single trees for shading stock or windbreaks. Screening of farm buildings. Eligible only under an improvement plan and when carried out in association with eligible building works. Grant is available even when screening is a condition of planning consent.	Up to 50% (Discretionary)	On sites up to ¼ ha in open countryside. Grant aid is also available for the screening of farm buildings but not when this is a condition of planning permission.	Nil	

Eligible works	Forestry Commission and NI Forest Service		MAFF, DAFS, DANI and WOAD		Countryside Commission, Countryside Commission for Scotland‡		Nature Conservancy Council‡	
	Grant	Points	Grant	Points	Grant	Points	Grant	Points
Woodland planting and management and/or shelter belts	Fixed rates per ha	Woodland Grant Scheme One sites over ¼ ha, 70% of grant paid on completion of planting. 20% paid after 5 years and balance of 10% 10 years after payment of first instalment, provided that plantation has been properly maintained. For natural regeneration the instalments will be 50%, 30%, 20%. See scheme booklet for details of timing. Timber production need not be the main objective.	60% 30%* or 15% 85%	LFA Other Eligible where planted as shelterbelt for agricultural or horticultural purpose. *The higher rate of grant applies outside the LFA where the shelter belt contains at least 50% broadleaved species. Crofting counties	Up to 50% (Discretionary)	On sites up to ¼ ha in open countryside.	Discretionary up to 50% of acceptable costs.	Applies only to work whose primary objective is to enhance wildlife habitat(s) or species on sites of high conservation importance.
Pollarding of riparian willows and alders (Not applicable in Scotland)	Nil		Nil		Up to 50% (Discretionary)	Aimed at schemes which include a number of trees in single ownership or action involving multiple land ownership within a single riparian zone.	Discretionary up to 50% of acceptable costs.	Applies only to works whose primary objective is to enhance wildlife habitat(s) or species on sites of high conservation importance.
Tree surgery	Nil		Nil		Up to 50% (Discretionary)	To extend life of visually important single tree or groups of trees. NB Costs involved demand close scrutiny of schemes and should preferably form part of replanting proposals or a farm conservation plan.	Nil	

Eligible works	Forestry Commission and NI Forest Service		MAFF, DAFS, DANI and WOAD		Countryside Commission‡ / Countryside Commission for Scotland‡		Nature Conservancy Council‡	
	Grant	Points	Grant	Points	Grant	Points	Grant	Points
Hedgerows/ hedgebanks	Nil		LFA 60% Other 30%	Grant available only when establishing new or improving existing hedgerow/hedgebanks (not for repairs). Includes hedgelaying but not annual maintenance. Stiles and footbridges also included.	Up to 50% (Discretionary)	Hedgerows and hedgebanks which are visually important. The work should preferably be part of a farm conservation plan, for which advice has been sought and obtained. Includes hedgelaying but not annual maintenance.	Discretionary up to 50% of acceptable costs.	To enable establishment, improvement, maintenance (not annual) where the hedgerow/hedgebank is an integral part of a site of nature conservation importance.
Walls/stone hedges/dykes	Nil		LFA 60% Other 30% LFA 30% Other 15% 55%	For provision and replacement of walls and dykes using traditional material but not for repairs/maintenance. Includes the provision of stiles and footbridges. Under an improvement plan only. For improvement and provision and replacement of walls and dykes using non-traditional materials but not for repairs or maintenance. Also includes provision of stiles and footbridges. Crofting counties	Up to 50% (Discretionary)	Visually important stone walls, improvement of which is preferably part of a farm conservation plan for which advice has been sought and obtained.	Discretionary up to 50% of acceptable costs.	To enable replacement, improvement, and repairs (not annual). Includes provision of stiles, gates and footbridges. The feature must be an integral part of a site of nature conservation importance.

Eligible works	Forestry Commission and NI Forest Service		MAFF, DAFS, DANI and WOAD		Countryside Commission‡ Countryside Commission for Scotland‡		Nature Conservancy Council‡	
	Grant	Points	Grant	Points	Grant	Points	Grant	Points
Fencing	Fixed rate per ha	Only as part of planting scheme. Fixed grant rate intended to cover fencing costs.	Grant aid towards the cost of temporary protective fencing to assist the establishment of a shelterbelt, windbreak or hedge is available at the appropriate rate of grant. Refer to individual features. LFA 30% Other 15% Other fencing is available for grant only if part of an improvement plan. Crofting counties 55%		Up to 50% (Discretionary)	As part of amenity tree planting, woodland management scheme or landscape conservation scheme.	Discretionary up to 50% of acceptable costs.	The works must provide direct or indirect benefit in the management of wildlife habitat(s) or species on sites of nature conservation importance.
Green lanes (Not applicable in Scotland)	Nil		Improvement or replacement of hedges, fencing and walls along green lanes eligible at appropriate rates of grant. Refer to individual features. LFA 20% Other 15% Surface of lane eligible for grant aid when it provides access for agricultural purposes and when part of an improvement plan.		Up to 50% (Discretionary)	Preferably as part of proposals for a farm conservation plan or when scheme involves a lane passing through several land ownerships.	Nil	

Eligible works	Forestry Commission and NI Forest Service		MAFF, DAFS, DANI and WOAD			Countryside Commission / Countryside Commission for Scotland‡		Nature Conservancy Council‡	
	Grant	Points	Grant	Points		Grant	Points	Grant	Points
Pond works	Nil		LFA 30% Other 15%	Grant available for pond works, as part of scheme to improve field drainage or for the storage of water. Work must be part of an improvement plan. Grant not available for maintenance.		Up to 50% (Discretionary)	When pond and immediate surrounding area is an important landscape feature and preferably part of a farm conservation plan. To desilt/bring back under management existing ponds and to create new ponds as landscape features.	Discretionary up to 50% of acceptable costs.	When pond and/or immediate surrounding area is of nature conservation importance. Includes management works (or exceptionally the creation of new ponds) designed to ensure retention and/or enhancement of nature conservation value.
Ditches	Nil		LFA 30% Other 15% Crofting counties 55% to 65%	As part of new field drainage scheme or improvement to an existing system and as part of an improvement plan.		Nil		Discretionary up to 50% of acceptable costs.	The works must be designed to retain or enhance existing wildlife interest in the ditch or nearby features of conservation importance.
Heather management	Nil		LFA 30% Other 15%	To encourage more vigorous growth of heather by burning or cutting. Regeneration of grass by burning.		Nil		Discretionary up to 50% of acceptable costs.	Applies only to work whose primary objective is to enhance wildlife habitat(s) or species of high conservation importance.
Bracken control	Nil		LFA 30% Other 15% Crofting counties 60%	Control must be by mechanical or chemical means not by ploughing.		Nil		Possible	See above

Section 11
Regulations Concerning Trees and Farm Woodlands

Section 11 Regulations Concerning Trees and Farm Woodlands

11.1 Purchase of Plants

The Forest Reproductive Material Regulations

The sale of planting stock of most of the major forest species is subject to the provisions of the Forest Reproductive Material Regulations. These are designed to ensure that the origins of the seed from which plants have been raised meet specified standards. Nurserymen and others selling planting stock of the species covered by the regulations are obliged to provide a Supplier's Certificate to purchasers on which details of the origin, etc., of the planting stock are given.

The Forest Reproductive Material Regulations are based on EEC Directives, and similar legislation applies to those selling tree seed and plants in other Community countries.

11.2 Felling Regulations

The felling of trees in Great Britain (but not in Northern Ireland or the inner London Boroughs) is controlled by the Forestry Commission in exercise of its powers under the Forestry Act 1967. A licence from the Commission is normally required to fell growing trees (though not for topping or lopping), but in any calendar quarter up to 5 cubic metres may be felled by an occupier without a licence provided not more than 2 cubic metres are sold.

Certain types of felling are exempt. The most important of these are as follows:

1. the felling is in accordance with an approved plan of operations under one of the Forestry Commission's grant schemes;
2. the trees are in a garden, orchard, churchyard or public open space;
3. the trees are below 8 centimetres in diameter, measured 1.3 metres from the ground; or in the case of thinnings, below 10 centimetres in diameter; or in the case of coppice or underwood, below 15 centimetres in diameter;
4. the trees are interfering with permitted development or statutory works by public bodies;
5. the trees are dead, dangerous, causing a nuisance or are badly affected by Dutch elm disease;
6. the felling is in compliance with an Act of Parliament.

In certain circumstances – whether or not a felling licence is needed – special permission may be required from another body for any proposed felling. This can occur where an area is designated as a Conservation Area or as a Site of Special Scientific Interest (SSSI) or the trees are covered by a Tree Preservation Order (TPO). In these cases, the bodies that would be involved are respectively, the District Council, the Nature Conservancy Council, and the Local Planning Authority.

Unless covered by one of the exceptions above (which are more fully set out in the Forestry Act 1967 and related Regulations), any felling undertaken without a licence is an offence and carries a liability to a fine not exceeding £1,000 or twice the value of the trees, whichever is the higher.

In addition, the Forestry Commission is empowered to serve a notice on an owner or tenant convicted of an illegal felling to restock the land concerned, or such other land as may be agreed, and to maintain the replacement trees in accordance with the rules and practice of good forestry for a period of up to 10 years.

Where a person fails to comply with the conditions of a felling licence or a restocking notice, the Forestry Commission may issue an enforcement notice requiring action to be taken to meet the conditions. Failure to carry out the action specified in the enforcement notice may result in the Commission entering on the land, carrying out the work and recovering the expenses incurred from the person on whom the notice was served. It is an offence not to comply with an enforcement notice and this carries a liability to a fine not exceeding £2,000.

Fuller details on Felling Licensing Regulations and Procedures are contained in the Forestry Commission booklet *Control of tree felling* available free from any Forestry Commission office.

11.3 Movement of Felled Timber – Disease Control

Movement of spruce wood – *Dendroctonus micans*

As a result of an outbreak of *Dendroctonus micans* (the great spruce bark beetle), controls are in force in Wales and the adjoining English counties + Lancashire (the Scheduled Area) which govern the movement of all wood of the spruce genus. Under powers imposed by the Restriction on Movement of Spruce Wood Order 1982 (as amended) it is unlawful for any person to move any spruce wood from a tree grown within the Scheduled Area to any place outside it or, unless the bark has been removed, along or across any highway within it. In certain circumstances, however, licences to permit the movement of spruce wood within the Scheduled Area can be obtained from the Forestry Commission. Such licences will impose conditions necessary to prevent spread of the pest. For example, spruce wood from infested stands can only be moved to mills specially 'approved' for the purpose and which have facilities for debarking logs and adequately treating the residues to prevent further infestation.

Dutch elm disease

Powers to enable certain local authorities to require owners to fell elms infected by Dutch elm disease are contained in the Dutch Elm Disease (Local Authorities) (Amendment) Order 1988. A sister order, the Dutch Elm Disease (Restriction on Movement of Elms) (Amendment) Order 1988, prohibits the movement of elm into any controlled area from any place outside it and also restricts the movement of elm within the controlled area to wood which has had the bark removed or to wood being moved in accordance with the terms of a licence issued by the Forestry Commission. A movement licence will contain conditions necessary to prevent spread of the beetle which carries the disease, and will specify the dates within which movement can take place and also the destination of the wood.

Details of areas covered by these Orders are available from the Forestry Commission to which application for licences to move elm wood should be addressed.

Watermark disease of cricket bat willow

Watermark disease (*Erwina salicis*) is a serious problem in the growing of cricket bat willow, and legislation exists to help reduce the spread of the disease. The Watermark Disease (Local Authorities) Order 1974, enables councils to serve notices on growers requiring the destruction of any infected material and to prohibit the sale of infected sets. This order covers the counties of Essex, Bedfordshire, Hertfordshire, Norfolk and Suffolk.

11.4 Farm Woodland Roads and Buildings

Construction of forestry roads and buildings is classed as development in terms of the Town and Country Planning Acts, but most such operations – as listed in class VII (Schedule 1) of the Town and Country Planning (General Development) Order 1977* – are classed as permitted development, and do not require specific application and approval. Exceptions to this general rule requiring specific approval by the local planning authority prior to commencement of work include.

1. Any buildings or road within 25 metres of the metalled portion of a trunk or classified road. (See Class VII of GDO.)*
2. Any building or works which exceed 3 metres in height, if within 3 km of the perimeter of an aerodrome. (See Class VII of GDO.)*
3. The siting, design and external appearance of forestry roads and buildings in National Parks and certain areas adjoining the Peak District, Lake District and Snowdonia Parks (Town and Country Planning (Agricultural and Forestry Development in National Parks, etc.) Special Development Order – 1986).
4. In National Scenic Areas (Scotland) planning permission is required for construction of forestry vehicle tracks, except for those which form part of an approved afforestation scheme. It is also required for forestry buildings and structures which exceed 12 metres in height. (Town and Country Planning (Restriction of Permitted Development) (National Scenic Areas) (Scotland) Direction 1987).
5. In Northern Ireland agricultural developments do not require planning permission provided that the nearest part of any building erected is not more than 75 metres from an existing group of buildings. However, there is control over certain types of development (including agricultural and forestry development) which applies to all buildings and structures over 12 metres high and exceeding 300

* In Scotland, Class VI (Schedule 1) of the Town and Country Planning (General Development) (Scotland) Order 1981.

square metres in ground area or within 24 metres of a Class 1 or 2 roads or within 9 metres of any road.

The need for other consents should also be considered, including Building Regulations, title conditions, lease conditions, Water Authority (or, in Scotland, River Purification Board) discharge consent, etc.

If there is any doubt as to whether or not proposed developments would require planning permission, then the local planning authority should be approached.

Section 12
Training and Safety Requirements

Section 12 Training and Safety Requirements

A legal obligation has been placed on employers, by virtue of Section 2 of the Health and Safety at Work etc. Act 1974, to provide adequate instruction, training and supervision as is necessary to ensure, so far as is reasonably practicable, the health and safety at work of their employees.

In the case of work being carried out by a person who is self-employed, Section 3(2) of the same Act stipulates that every self-employed person shall conduct his undertakings in such a way as to ensure, so far as is reasonably practicable, that he and other persons who may be affected thereby are not exposed to risks to their health and safety.

There is thus no lack of legal framework for the requirement to train and indeed this has recently been extended by the requirements for skill and competence to be displayed by all users of pesticides (The Control of Pesticides Regulations 1986).

Training should not, however, be undertaken merely on the grounds of fulfilling a legal obligation which in most cases is concerned with the requirement to work safely. The aims and benefits of training must be in the context of improving professional competence and productivity. Training must also be systematic whereby it is designed to make good identifiable deficiencies and not as a panacea for unidentified gaps in knowledge and skills.

Many farmers intending to create new woodlands or restore existing neglected woodlands will require training in silvicultural techniques and woodland management. Those who decide to do the resultant practical work will need to acquire the necessary skills.

The Forestry Commission's Education and Training Branch has designed a one week course on Farm Woodland Management dealing with *inter alia*:

selecting management objectives
site assessment
timber inventory
choice of species
silvicultural techniques
costing of operations
assessment of harvesting potential
preparation of contracts
valuation of standing and felled timber
criteria for admission to grant schemes

This course framework can readily be extended to include practical demonstrations of site preparation, protection, planting, weed control and maintenance. However, for those farmers who wish to go beyond this demonstrational approach in order to acquire practical skills, then the Forestry Training Council (recognised by MSC as the Non Statutory Training Organisation for the Forestry Industry), can co-ordinate demand and arrange for training to be provided in the following subjects: planting and beating-up, hand or mechanical draining, weed control (hand, chemical or mechanical), cleaning, pruning, harvesting with chain saw, conversion by either chain saw or circular saw, extraction by skidder or tractor/trailer combination.

Skills training is also being undertaken by several colleges which are 'Approved Training Organisations' under MSC criteria for conducting Youth Training Schemes. The addresses of these establishments together with that of the Forestry Training Council are given in Appendix C.

Mention has already been made of the Health and Safety at Work etc. Act (1974) and of the more recent Control of Pesticides Regulations 1986. It should additionally be noted that by definition forestry operations also fall within the scope of The Agriculture (Safety, Health and Welfare) Act 1956 and the various regulations made thereunder, e.g. Field Machinery, Circular Saws and Stationary Machinery. Forestry tractors also come within the scope of the several legal requirements imposed by the Tractor Cabs Regulations 1970 and 1974. Detailed advice on the application of these enactments in forestry can be obtained from area offices of the Health and Safety Executive although comprehensive guidance has been defined and published by the Forestry Safety Council in FSC leaflets. These are currently available covering the following operations.

N Noise and hearing conservation
1. Clearing saw
2. ULV herbicide spraying
3. Application of herbicide by knapsack spraying
4. Application of granular herbicide
6. Tractor mounted weeding machines
7. Planting
8. Hand weeding
9. Brashing and pruning with handsaw
10. The chain saw
11. Felling by chain saw
12. Chain saw snedding

13. Chain saw – crosscutting and stacking
14. Chain saw – take down of hung-up trees
15. Chain saw – clearance of windblow
17. Chain saw – felling large hardwoods
18. Tree climbing and pruning
21. Forest tractors
22. Extraction by skidder
23. Extraction by forwarder
24. Processor (limber bucker)
25. Extraction by cable crane
26. Use of tractors with winches in directional felling and takedown
30. Mobile saw bench
31. Mobile peeling machine

32. Fencing
33. Hand held power posthole borer
34. First aid
35. All-terrain cycles

The leaflets are available free of charge from the Secretary whose address is given in Appendix C.

Whilst these FSC guides have no particular legal status they are nonetheless used by the enforcement authority (HSE) as one of several criteria in deciding whether a breach has been committed. Their content has been successfully used in evidence during legal proceedings.

Appendices

APPENDIX A
Glossary of Woodland Terms and Abbreviations Used in the Text

Agroforestry – a system producing both forestry and agricultural (animal or plant) crops in an intimate mixture from the same land.

AIS – Agricultural Improvement Scheme, a capital grant scheme introduced on 1 October 1985 under EC regulation 797/85

Apical dominance – growth concentrated on the leader (or top shoot which is a straight extension of the main stem) which produces a straight stem.

APR – annual percentage rate of interest

Arboriculture – the cultivation and tending of trees, individually or in small groups, for use and ornament.

Beating-up – replacement of failures in a newly planted tree crop (normally done at yearly intervals after planting).

Blinding – spreading of fine gravel or small stone chippings to seal the surface of a road or track.

Bole – the trunk or main stem of the tree.

Brashing – pruning away all branches from the lower trunk (normally up to 2 or 3 m) of plantation grown trees.

Canopy – collectively, the mass of branches and foliage formed by the crowns of trees.

Cleaning – removal of unwanted woody species (which have usually arrived by natural regeneration or have regrown from cut stumps) from amongst young crop trees.

Clear felling – complete removal of the whole tree crop at one time.

Clone – a genetically uniform group of plants originating from a single plant by vegetative reproduction.

Coppice (n) (copse) – woodland consisting of stools of broadleaved trees that gives rise to successive crops of poles and sticks, when cut over on a rotation.

Coppice (v) – i. to fell trees close to the ground with the intention of producing coppice shoots from the stools.
ii. to produce coppice shoots.
iii. to harvest the coppice shoots as a crop of poles and stakes.

Crown – the canopy of branches of the tree.

Cultivar – an internationally agreed term of a cultivated variety, variety being a sub-division of a species, consisting of plants which differ in some heritable characters such as form, colour or season, from what is regarded as typical of the species, also applied to members of a hybrid group.

DA – land designated as less favoured in February 1984. (See under LFA). In terms of handicaps to farming it is less severely disadvantaged than land in SDAs.

dbh – (mean diameter breast height) the mean diameter of trees measured at 1.3 m above ground level.

DE – discounted expenditure, the present value of all future costs of a project, taking into account the different times at which they occur.

Disbudding – removal of buds, usually to stop the growth of epicormics or to ensure apical dominance.

Discounting – the process of reducing future sums of money to take into account the delay in time before they are spent or received. Discounting is the opposite of compounding but works on the same principle, giving a present value (or discounted value) to amounts arising in the future.

Double mould board plough – a plough which throws out two ridges from a single furrow as opposed to the single mould board which produces a single ridge of overturned turf.

DR – discounted revenue, as for discounted expenditure but dealing with incomes rather than costs.

EC – European Community in the context of this Bulletin the European Economic Community or Common Market.

Epicormic shoots – secondary growth from dormant or adventitious buds on the stem or main branches. Should not be confused with suckers.

ESA – Environmentally Sensitive Area as designated by Ministers under their Powers Granted by Section 18 of the Agriculture Act 1986.

Favoured – selected for retention during thinning and given favourable treatment by removing competing trees.

Forwarder – a trailer system where shortwood is carried fully suspended on the trailer and loaded by means of a knuckle boom loader.

FSC – Forestry Safety Guide, issued by the Forestry Safety Council (see Section 12).

FWS – Farm Woodland Scheme (see Section 10.1).

GDP – gross domestic production. A measure of the total flow of goods and services produced by the economy over a particular time period, normally a year.

Gley – a soil formed under conditions of poor drainage and waterlogged all or part of the time.

Grieve – farm foreman (in Scotland).

Hardwood – the timber of any broadleaved tree whether actually hard or not. In common usage, broadleaved.

High forest – a forest consisting of maiden trees, being allowed to reach full height with a closed and high canopy.

Hoppus foot – an imperial volume measure used in the timber trade (see Appendix B).

HSE – Health and Safety Executive (see Section 12). The Government agency responsible for enforcement of health and safety legislation.

Increment – see MAI.

IRR – Internal Rate of Return. The rate of interest which, when used to discount the cash flow associated with an investment project, reduces its net present value to zero. Hence it provides a measure of the earning power or break-even rate of return of an investment.

LFA – less favoured areas designated by the European Community in Directive 84/169/EEC. This designation was made under the Less Favoured Areas Directive, 72/268/EEC, which provides special measures to assist farming in the areas designated.

Live crown – the part of the tree's crown which is still alive and capable of bearing trees.

MAI – Mean Annual Volume Increment. This is the total volume production to date, divided by the age, i.e. the average rate of volume production over the life of the crop to date.

Maidens – a young seedling tree which has not been cut back.

Mound planting – planting a tree with its roots in a mound of earth thrown up to ensure good aeration, free drainage and less competition. This technique is often used on wet ground by turning over turves or more usually by spreading out dollops of soil/peat with a backhoe or excavator.

Mulching – the application of a layer of suitable material to the surface of the soil to conserve moisture, reduce soil temperature fluctuations and suppress weed growth around a young tree.

NPV – Net Present Value. This is the surplus of discounted benefit over the discounted cost from a project. It may be negative if costs outweigh benefits. It represents profit or return from the investment, at the given discount rate, and is a measure of the project's desirability.

Nurse (crop) – a crop of trees grown to encourage the growth of another species by protecting the latter from, for example, wind, frost or strong sunlight.

Pit planting – planting in a pit of prepared or cultivated soil.

Planting model – See Section 4.

Pole stage – a stage in the growth of young trees at which the crowns are above head height, but the timber taken out in thinnings, etc., is below the size of saw timber.

Processor – a multifunctional machine, also known as a limber-bucker, which removes the branches, cross cuts to shortwood and cuts off the top of the felled trees.

Pruning – the removal of live branches from the stem so that subsequent growth produces a cylinder of knot free timber around a knotty stem core. Pruning is usually confined to the main crop trees to produce quality timber.

Pulpwood – timber which is destined to be used for the production of wood pulp (for paper or board manufacture). Generally small roundwood in 2 or 3 metre lengths.

Rack – a narrow unpaved pathway left or cut through a tree crop to give access and to facilitate the extraction of timber to a wide ride or road.

Recruited – usually applied to trees arising from natural regeneration which are recruited into (chosen to form part of) the (planted) crop of trees.

Sawlogs – timber of a size and quality suitable for conversion in a saw mill, e.g. a large straight log, bole or branch.

Scarify – see screefing.

Screefing – scraping off the organic layer and vegetation from the soil surface to expose the mineral soil.

SDA – in general the most severely disadvantaged land within the LFAs, when measured in terms of handicap to farming (see LFA).

Selection forestry – the system of growing trees in an intimate mixture of ages and often species producing a mixed aged woodland from which only a few trees are ever removed at one time.

Shortwood – felled trees cut into short lengths at the stump before extraction to the road or rideside.

Short rotation coppice – woody species grown on a very short rotation (less than 10 and usually 3 to 5 years) with the crop being harvested and chipped with the chips being used for energy production (burnt for fuel) in the simplest system.

Skidder – a tractor used to extract timber from the stump to the ride or roadside by dragging (skidding) all or part of the load along the ground.

Silviculture – the growing and tending of trees in woodlands, plantations or natural forests.

Single mould board plough – see double mould board plough.

Singled – reduced to a single stem. Usually applied to coppice stools where several stems may be cut off to leave just one stem to grow on.

Small roundwood – small diameter timber which is usually too small to be sawn and is used in the round for poles, stakes, pulp or chipwood.

Softwood – timber derived from, or alternative name for, coniferous trees.

SSSI – Site of Special Scientific Interest. These are sites designated, because of their outstanding scientific interest and value, by the Nature Conservancy Council as part of their responsibilities under the Wildlife and Countryside Act 1987. On designated SSSIs certain operations listed as potentially damaging may be prohibited except by agreement with the Nature Conservancy Council. In Northern Ireland areas of special scientific interest (ASSIs) are designated by the Department of the Environment under the Nature Conservancy and Amenity Lands (Northern Ireland) Order 1985.

Stag-headed – trees with dead branches protruding from the top of the live crown as a result of injury, old age, disease or fluctuations in water supply.

Stand – a group of trees, often applied to groups of trees of the same age.

Standards – i. individual or widely spaced trees left to grow on to maturity often with coppice or a successor generation growing under and between them (maiden).
ii. a plant with an upright clean stem supporting a head. Plants in standard form are described, in descending order according to the height of the clear stem, as tall standard, standard and ½ standard.

Stools – see coppice.

Stumping back – cutting back the stems of maidens (see above) to induce the formation of a coppice stool.

Suckers – woody shoots arising from an underground stem or root, or shoots arising from the understock of a worked (grafted or budded) plant.

Sun scorch – damage caused to bark by unaccustomed exposure to the sun, for example, following the sudden removal of shade.

Thicket stage – a stage in the growth of a plantation or natural regeneration during which the lower branches of the growing trees meet and interlace.

Thinning – the removal, at certain stages of growth, of a proportion of trees from a crop. For example, to allow the remainder more growing space or to obtain a supply of timber.

> *crown thinning* – removal of neighbouring trees which are interfering with the development of the best crowns in the crop.
> *heavy thinning* – thinning which removes a relatively high proportion of the trees from the crop as opposed to light thinning – a low proportion.
> *line thinning* – removal of complete rows, often used initially as an alternative to brashing as a way of gaining access to a crop.
> *low thinning* – thinning in which the removals are confined to inferior stems.
> *selective thinning* – individual selection and marking of the trees to be removed.

Top height – the average total height of the 100 trees of largest diameter per hectare.

TPO – Tree Preservation Order – Orders made by the local planning authority under the Town and Country Planning (Tree Preservation Order) Regulations. The purpose of a TPO is to protect specified trees and woodland from wilful damage and destruction and to prevent the felling, topping, lopping or uprooting of trees covered by an Order without consent of the authority.

Transplants – any plant which has been transplanted one or more times in the nursery. This is done to develop a better root:shoot ratio than would be the case if the trees were allowed to grow undisturbed from the time of sowing to the time when they are planted out in the wood.

Treeshelter – plastic tubes placed around newly planted trees to encourage fast early growth and offer some protection from mammals and chemical sprays.

ULV – Ultra Low Volume – applies to the amount of spray solution (diluent plus herbicide) applied per unit area. ULV is the term applied to spraying rates below 10 litres per hectare.

Underwood – the lower storey in a high forest, often coppice being grown under standards.

Unrooted sets – short lengths (up to 0.5 m) of stem cut from regrowth (up to 3 years old) of poplar or willow, which are inserted straight into the ground. These then form roots and grow to form young trees.

Veneer quality timber – timber which is of high quality to be sliced for veneer production. Usually this means that the log must be above a minimum diameter and branch and knot free. Knot free timber is produced by early pruning so that only a narrow core of knotty wood is left inside a cylinder of undisturbed wood.

Whip – a young tree consisting only of a single slender stem, usually of one or two years' growth.

Windthrow– blowing down of trees by the wind.

Yield class – see Section 7.

Yield model – see Section 7.

APPENDIX B
Conversion Factors

In the main a knowledge and understanding of metric units has been assumed throughout this book. However, farmers will still find, especially when dealing with the timber trade, that some prices, etc., will be quoted with reference to imperial units; and that the trade has some units exclusively applicable to timber such as hoppus feet. For a fuller set of metric conversion tables Forestry Commission Booklet 30 should be referred to. The main factors are as follows.

Length

Millimetres to inches
1 mm = 0.0393701 in
1 in = 25.4 mm

Centimetres diameter to inches quarter girth
1 cm diam = 0.309212 in q g
1 in q g = 3.23403 cm diam

Centimetres diameter to inches girth
1 cm diam = 1.23685 in girth
1 in girth = 0.808507 cm diam

Metres to feet
1 m = 3.28084 ft
1 ft = 0.3048 m

Metres to yards
1 m = 1.09361 yd
1 yd = 0.9144 m

Area

Square metres to square yards
$1 \text{ m}^2 = 1.19599 \text{ yd}^2$
$1 \text{ yd}^2 = 0.836127 \text{ m}^2$

Hectares to acres
1 ha = 2.47105 acres
1 acre = 0.404686 ha

Volume

Cubic metres to cubic feet
$1 \text{ m}^3 = 35.3147 \text{ ft}^3$
$1 \text{ ft}^3 = 0.0283168 \text{ m}^3$

Cubic metres to hoppus feet
$1 \text{ m}^3 = 27.7361 \text{ h ft}$
$1 \text{ h ft} = 0.0360541 \text{ m}^3$

Cubic metres to cubic yards
$1 \text{ m}^3 = 1.30795 \text{ yd}^3$
$1 \text{ yd}^3 = 0.764555 \text{ m}^3$

Cubic metres per hectare to hoppus feet per acre
$1 \text{ m}^3/\text{ha} = 11.2244 \text{ h ft/acre}$
$1 \text{ h ft/acre} = 0.089091 \text{ m}^3/\text{ha}$

Cubic metres per tonne to hoppus feet per ton
$1 \text{ m}^3/\text{tonne} = 28.1812 \text{ h ft/ton}$
$1 \text{ h ft/ton} = 0.0354847 \text{ m}^3/\text{tonne}$

Capacity

Litres to gallons (British)
1 litre = 0.219969 gal
1 gal = 4.54609 litres

Litres per hectare to gallons (British) per acre
1 litre/ha = 0.0890184 gal/acre
1 gal/acre = 11.2336 litres/ha

Mass

Grammes to ounces, avoir
1 g = 0.035274 oz
1 oz = 28.3495 g

Kilogrammes to pounds, avoir
1 kg = 2.20462 lb
1 lb = 0.453592 kg

Tonnes, metric to tons, British
1 tonne = 0.984207 ton
1 ton = 1.101605 tonne

Fertilisers

Nitrogen fertilisers

Name	Formula	% N declared	Remarks
Sulphate of ammonia (ammonium sulphate)	$(NH_4)_2SO_4$	20.6	Crystalline
Nitro-chalk	$NH_4NO_3 + CaCO_3$	21	Must be stored in moisture proof containers
Nitram	NH_4NO_3	34.5	

Phosphorus fertilisers

Name	% P_2O_5 (P) approx	Remarks
Superphosphate	$18-20$ $(8-9)$	Granular or powdered
Triple super-phosphate	44(19) and 47(21)	Granular
Mineral or rock phosphate	$27-29$ $(12-13)$	Name usually indicates source, e.g. Gafsa (Tunis)
Basic slag	$6-22$ $(3-10)$	Raises pH, especially slags with low % total P_2O_5

Potassium fertilisers

Name	Formula	% K_2O (K) approx	Remarks
Sulphate of potash (potassium sulphate)	K_2SO_4	50(42)	Crystalline
Muriate of potash (potassium chloride)	KC1	60(50)	Must be stored in moisture proof containers

APPENDIX C
Sources of Advice

Farm woodland advice

A wide range of advice on farm woodlands, including the Farm Woodland Scheme, is available from the local offices of the agricultural departments (ADAS advisers, or Agricultural Inspectors in Northern Ireland). In Scotland, this advice is available from the Scottish Agricultural Colleges (SAC) Advisory Service; DAFS staff will provide information on the Farm Woodland Scheme. Advice is also available from the local offices of the Forestry Commission or the Northern Ireland Forest Service. All enquirers seeking information on the Farm Woodland Scheme will be sent an information pack and application form.

Advisers from the agricultural departments, SAC Advisory Service, Forestry Commission private woodlands staff and the Forest Service in Northern Ireland will provide advice at the general level, free of charge. For detailed advice on a particular scheme and assistance with plan preparation and submission, the agricultural departments and SAC Advisory Service will make a charge.

Detailed advice and assistance may also be sought on a charged basis from private forestry consultants or forestry management companies and farmers can obtain lists of these by writing to the following.

The Institute of Chartered Foresters
22 Walker Street, Edinburgh, EH3 7HR
Tel: 031 225 2705

The Royal Institution of Chartered Surveyors
12 Great George Street, London, SW1P 3AD
Tel: 01 222 7000

The Association of Professional Foresters
Brokerswood House, Brokerswood, Nr Westbury, Wiltshire, BA13 4EH
Tel: 0373 822238

In addition two organisations have been set up in recent years specifically to investigate and provide advice on existing farm woodlands, these are:

Project Sylvanus (covers Dean, Cornwall and Somerset)
Office One, Poole House, 16 Pool Road, Bodmin, Cornwall, PL31 2HB
Tel: 0208 4330

Coed Cymru (covers Wales)
Ladywell House, Newton, Powys, SY16 1RD
Tel: 0686 26799

Nine of the 11 Welsh County Councils have Coed Cymru project officers on staff who are able to provide advice to farmers. As well as these, many local authorities have forestry experts on their staff responsible for administration of Countryside Commission grant schemes as well as the provision of advice.

Arboricultural advice

The Arboricultural Association will supply free of charge a copy of their Directory of Consultants and Contractors who will provide expert advice or deal with trees around farm buildings, near roads, power lines or individual specimen trees.

The Secretary
The Arboricultural Association, Ampfield House, Nr Romsey, Hampshire, S051 9PA
Tel: 0794 68717

Recreation advice

Specialised advice on farm woods and recreation may be sought from the local offices of the Countryside Commissions (England and Wales or Scotland). These should be listed in the telephone directory but in case of difficulty the National Headquarters are:

Countryside Commission (England and Wales)
John Dower House, Crescent Place, Cheltenham, Gloucestershire, GL50 3RA
Tel: 0242 521381

Countryside Commission for Scotland
Battleby, Redgorton, Perth, PH1 3EW
Tel: 0738 27921

Advice on landscape design

Farmers seeking professional advice on landscape design should contact the Landscape Institute who will provide a register of landscape practices.

The Landscape Institute
12 Carlton House Terrace, London, SW1Y 5AH
Tel: 01 839 4044

Conservation advice

Specialist advice on conservation in relation to farm woods may be obtained from local Nature Conservancy Council offices or local Farming, Forestry and Wildlife Advisory Groups. These addresses should be available in local telephone directories but in case of difficulty the national addresses are as follows:

Nature Conservancy Council
Northminster House, Peterborough, PE1 1UA
Tel: 0733 40345

Nature Conservancy Council
12 Hope Terrace, Edinburgh, EH9 2AS
Tel: 031 447 4784

Farming and Wildlife Trust Ltd (managing body for FFWAGs)
The Lodge, Sandy, Bedfordshire, SG19 2DL
Tel: 0767 80551

The address covers all 65 groups in England, Wales, Scotland and Northern Ireland. Alternatively the name and address of local FFWAG advisers may be obtained through local agricultural department advisers.

Sporting advice

Technical advice on all aspects of game conservation and shoot management including woodland siting, planting and design is available from:

The Game Conservancy
Fordingbridge, Hampshire, SP6 1EF
Tel: 0425 52381

or

The British Association for Shooting and Conservation
Marford Mill, Rossett, Wrexham, Clwyd, LL12 0HL
Tel: 0244 570881

For advice on the management of deer in farm woodlands The Game Conservancy or the British Deer Society should be approached.

The British Deer Society
Church Farm, Lower Basildon, Reading, Berkshire, RG8 9HH
Tel: 07357 4094

Colleges

The following are 'Approved Training Organisations' for Forestry Skills Training under MSC criteria for conducting Youth Training Schemes.

Inverness College of Further and Higher Education Scottish School of Forestry, 3 Longman Road, Longman South, Inverness, IV1 1SA
Tel: 0463 790 431

Barony Agricultural College, Parkgate, Dumfries, DG1 3NE
Tel: 038786 251

Cumbria College of Agriculture, Newton Rigg, Penrith, Cumbria, CA11 0AH
Tel: 0768 63791

Lincolnshire College of Agriculture, Riseholm, Lincoln, LN2 2LG
Tel: 0522 22252

Hereford College of Agriculture, Holme Lacy, Hereford, HR2 6LL
Tel: 043 273 282/316

Dartington Tech Limited, The Old Postern, Dartington, Totnes, Devon, TQ9 6EA
Tel: 0803 866051

Coleg Glynllifon, Clynnog Road, Caernarfon, Gwynedd, LL54 5DU
Tel: 0286 830261

The Forestry Training Council

The Secretary, The Forestry Training Council, 231 Corstorphine Road, Edinburgh, EH12 7AT
Tel: 031 334 8083

The Agricultural Training Board

The Secretary, The Agricultural Training Board, Bourne House, 32–34 Beckenham Road, Beckenham, Kent, BR3 4TB
Tel: 01 650 4890

The Forestry Safety Council

The Secretary, The Forestry Safety Council, 231 Corstorphine Road, Edinburgh, EH12 7AT
Tel: 031 334 0303

APPENDIX D
Planting Models for Other Woodland Systems

This Bulletin is aimed mainly at the type of small farm woodlands which are expected to be planted under the Farm Woodland Scheme. The first planting model provided in this appendix illustrates the layout which farmers might adopt to plan and cost the planting of such a wood using the information provided in Sections 3 and 4.

The remaining planting models contained in this appendix illustrate the rather different sets of operations required to establish the alternative systems covered in Section 2.

Table D.1 Planting model for budgeting

Operation	% of area treated	Year(s) of operation[1]	Labour £/ha	Machinery £/ha	Materials £/ha	Total cost £/ha
Establishment						
Ground preparation						
Road/track construction						
Initial drainage						
Fencing						
Planting		0				
Initial fertiliser						
Weeding						
Beating-up						
Grants WGS[2]		0				
Grants WGS		5				
Grants WGS		10				
FWS annual payments		1 to				
Maintenance						
General maintenance (drains, fences, etc.)						
Brashing						
Pruning						
Fire/storm insurance		0 to				
Management expenses						

1. The year convention adopted in planting models is that the year of planting is always described as year 0, the year before planting as year −1, 3 years after planting as year 3 and so on.
2. The initial payment under the Woodland Grant Scheme is payable immediately after planting. A second instalment is paid after 5 years, and a third instalment after 10 years, provided that the wood has been properly maintained.

Table D.2 Planting model example for agroforestry

This example assumes a broadleaved crop at a 10 metre spacing (100 trees per hectare). It does not include the inputs necessary from the agricultural part of the system.

Operation	% of area treated	Year(s) of operation[1]	Labour £/ha	Machinery £/ha	Materials £/ha	Total cost £/ha
Establishment						
Ground preparation[2]	100	−1	−2		−1	−3
Fencing[3]	100	0	−372	−35	−363	−770
Planting[4]	100	0	−100		−20	−120
Protection[4]	100	0			−130	−130
Weeding[5]	100	0	−10		−1	−11
Weeding[6]	100	1 to 3	−10		−2	−12
Pruning[7]	100	4,6,8,&10	−20			−20
Maintenance						
Fence and tree protection maintenance	100	5 to 35	−3	−4		−7
Misc maintenance	100	1 to 35	−1			−1

1. The year convention adopted in planting models is that the year of planting is always described as year 0, the year before planting as year − 1, 3 years after planting as year 3 and so on.
2. Ground preparation implies spot spraying the planting postions (100 per hectare) with glyphosate (Roundup) with a knapsack sprayer the summer before planting.
3. For the purposes of this example it has been assumed that this 4 ha wood has a perimeter of 1500 metres. At £205 per 100 metre (stock fencing) run this implies a cost of (15 × £205/4 ha) = £769 per hectare. Fencing is only required in addition to treeshelters as a normal field boundary to contain farm stock.
4. Planting, staking and protection are usually carried out as a single operation. A single broadleaved transplant is notch planted beside a tanalised fencing stake (1.7 m × 70 mm × 70 mm, 0.5 m into the ground) and protected by a treeshelter (1.2 m). A second stake (0.6 m) to which the shelter is to be secured is driven in most of its length at the gap side of the shelter. This protection assumes sheep rearing. If cattle are kept then 2.0 m treeshelters will be needed and the first stake will need to be 2.5 m × 70 mm × 70 mm.
5. In the first summer after planting glyphosate is applied with a knapsack sprayer (the treeshelter will prevent contact with the tree) to an area one metre in diameter at the base of each tree, at a rate of 1.5 litres per *treated* hectare.
6. In the winter following planting, and in the two winters after that, propyzamide granules are applied around the base of each tree at the rate of 37.5 kg per *treated* hectare.
7. Pruning takes place every other year, starting in the 4th, until there are about 5 metres of clean stem. In any one pruning about two-thirds of the tree should be left in crown.

   Normally pruning is best done during the winter. However, for some species (cherry, walnut and poplar) this is inappropriate and pruning is best done in June and July.

Table D.3 Planting model example for poplar

This example assumes a 4 hectare wood with a planting density of 156 trees per hectare (8 metre spacing).

Operation	% of area treated	Year(s) of operation[1]	Labour £/ha	Machinery £/ha	Materials £/ha	Total cost £/ha
Establishment						
Ground preparation[2]	100	0	−14	−18		−32
Fencing[3]	100	0	−372	−35	−363	−770
Planting[4]	100	0	−150		−30	−180
Protection[4]	100	0			−130	−130
Weeding[5]	100	0	−15		−1	−16
Weeding[6]	100	1 to 2	−15		−3	−18
Pruning[7]	100	3 & 5	−30			−30
Pruning[8]	100	7,9 &11	−15			−15
Grants WGS[9]	100	0				+115
Grants WGS	100	5				+33
Grants WGS	100	10				+16
FWS annual payments	100	1 to 30				+190
Maintenance						
Fence maintenance	100	5 to 35	−2			−2
Misc maintenance	100	1 to 35	−1			−1

1. The year convention adopted in planting models is that the year of planting is always described as year 0, the year before planting as year − 1,3 years after planting as year 3 and so on.
2. Ground preparation consists of a complete ploughing with an agricultural plough. As an alternative, individual planting positions may be prepared using a tractor-mounted post hole borer. Ploughing is likely to be cheaper.
3. For the purposes of this example it has been assumed that this 4 ha wood has a perimeter of 1500 metres. At £205 per 100 metre (stock fencing) run this implies a cost of (15 × 205/4 ha) = £769 per hectare. Fencing would only be required in conjunction with the treeshelter where there are stock on the farm.
4. Planting, staking and protection are usually carried out as a single operation. A 0.25 metre cutting is inserted to a depth of 0.2 metre beside a tanalised fencing stake (1.7 m × 70 mm × 70 mm) and protected by a treeshelter (1.2 m).
5. In the first summer after planting glyphosate is applied with a knapsack sprayer (the treeshelter will prevent contact with the tree) to an area one metre in diameter at the base of each tree, at a rate of 1.5 litres per *treated* hectare.
6. In the first and second winters following planting, propyzamide granules are applied around the base of each tree at the rate of 37.5 kg per *treated* hectare.
7. Pruning starts in year 3. In any one pruning two-thirds of the tree should be left in crown. This operation should take place in June. The first and second pruning take about twice as long as subsequent prunings.
8. Pruning continues until there are 6 metres of clean bole. From the 3rd pruning onwards the trees may be showing epicormic shoots, that is young shoots growing from that part of the stem already pruned. These have to be removed.
9. The initial payment for the Woodland Grant Scheme is payable immediately after planting. A second and third instalment are paid in the 5th and 10th years, provided the wood has been properly maintained. Wide spaced poplar is allowed within the Scheme because this is the accepted silvicultural method for growing the species. However, because the spacing adopted in this example is in excess of the 3 m maximum for broadleaves under the Woodland Grant Scheme the grant payable has been reduced pro rata, i.e. the planting is 4 ha, therefore the grant band 3 applies which gives £1,175 per ha. 8 m spacing = 156 trees per ha compared with 3 m spacing which = 1111 trees per ha.

Grant payable is therefore $£1,175 \times \dfrac{156}{1111} = £164$ per hectare.

Table D.4 Planting model example for cricket bat willow

This example assumes that the willows will be planted at 15 metre spacing (that is 45 per hectare).

Operation	% of area treated	Year(s) of operation[1]	Labour £/ha	Machinery £/ha	Materials £/ha	Total cost £/ha
Establishment						
Ground preparation[2]	100	0	−21	−1		−22
Fencing[3]	100	0	−372	−35	−363	−770
Planting[4]	100	0	−60		−30	−90
Protection[4]	100	0			−50	−50
Weeding[5]	100	0 to 2	−6		−1	−7
Disbudding[6]	100	1	−18			−18
Disbudding	100	2 & 3	−6			−6

1. The year convention adopted in planting models is that the year of planting is always described as year 0, the year before planting as year − 1, 3 years after planting as year 3 and so on.
2. Ground preparation consists of preparing the 45 planting postions per hectare with a tractor-mounted post hole borer.
3. For the purposes of this example it has been assumed that this 4 ha wood has a perimeter of 1500 metres. At £205 per 100 metre (stock fencing) run this implies a cost of (15 × £250/4 ha) = £769 per hectare. Fencing would only be required in addition to treeshelters on farms where there is stock
4. Planting, staking and protection are usually carried out as a single operation. An unrooted willow set (2.5 m to 3.0 m) is inserted 0.6 metres into the ground beside a tanalised stake (1.7 m × 70 mm × 70 mm, 0.5 m into the ground) and is tied close to the top of the stake. The tree is then protected against rabbits by a spiral guard, or, alternatively, a treeshelter may be used.
5. In the first summer after planting glyphosate is applied with a guarded knapsack sprayer to an area one metre in diameter at the base of each tree, at a rate of 1.5 litres per *treated* hectare.

   As an alternative to weeding a mulch may be used. The mulch should be 1 metre in diameter. It may be organic, or plastic sheeting, the latter being secured by inverted turves around the edge.

6. Each stem should be disbudded to 80% of its height until there are 2.5 metres of clear stem. In the first year there should be three visits during May and June. In the second and third year the operation needs to be done just once, preferably in May but it can be done in June.

Table D.5 Planting model example for coppice

Operation	% of area treated	Year(s) of operation[1]	Labour £/ha	Machinery £/ha	Materials £/ha	Total cost £/ha
Establishment						
Construction of roads	100	0	−14	−18		−32
Ground preparation[2]			−68	−32		−100
Fencing[3]	100	0	−190	−20	−190	−400
Planting[4]	100	0	−260		−340	−600
Weeding[5]	100	1	−24		−5	−29
Beating up[6]	100	1	−74		−106	−180
Grants WGS[7]	100	0				+823
Grants WGS	100	5				+235
Grants WGS	100	10				+117
FWS annual payments	100	1 to 10				+ 190
Maintenance						
Misc maintenance	100	1 to 45	−7	−1	−1	−9
First crop[8]	100	15				+125
Gapping up[9]	100	15	−37		−53	−90
Second crop[10]	100	30				+300
Gapping up	100	30	−37		−53	−90
Third crop[11]	100	45				+740
Gapping up	100	45	−37		−53	−90

1. The year convention adopted in planting models is that the year of planting is always described as year 0, the year before planting as year − 1,3 years after planting as year 3 and so on.
2. Ground preparation consists of ploughing with an agricultural plough with a density of furrows sufficient to match the planting space.
3. For the purpose of this example it has been assumed that this 5 ha wood has a perimeter of 925 metres. At £217 per 100 metre (rabbit fencing) run this implies a cost of (9.25 × £217/5 ha) = £401 per hectare.
4. Planting will be at a rate of 2000 per hectare. Plants are rather more expensive than normal at £170 per thousand.
5. Because this is a fertile site it has been assumed that grass and herbaceous weeds will develop during the first growing season and need treating. This has been costed as for glyphosate (Roundup) applied with a weedwiper, to avoid any risk of contact with the trees.
6. Beating up has been costed assuming that 20% of the trees died and needed replacing.
7. The initial payment in the Woodland Grant Scheme is payable immediately after planting. A second instalment is paid after 5 years, and a third instalment after 10 years, provided that the wood has been properly maintained. Farm Woodland Scheme payments for coppice run for 10 years only.
8. There will be few stems per stool at the first cutting. Although these will be of marketable quality, the volume will be relatively low.
9. About 5% of stools die after each cropping and need replacing.
10. The second cropping at 30 years yields considerably less than mature coppice plantations.
11. At the third cropping yields should be up to a maximum for the site.

Table D.6 Planting model example for short rotation coppice

Energy forestry is a new concept and it is still under investigation by the Department of Energy. Costs and returns are subject to further research.

Operation	% of area treated	Year(s) of operation[1]	Labour £/ha	Machinery £/ha	Materials £/ha	Total cost £/ha
Establishment						
Ground preparation Chemical[2]	100	0	−110	−10	−50	−170
Ground preparation Plough[3]	100	0	−35	−45		−80
Fencing[4]	100	0	−394	−37	−383	−814
Liming[5]						
Planting[6]	100	0	−400		−800	−1200
Weeding[7]	25	1	−50		−190	−240
Cutting back[8]	100	1	−72	−8		−80

1. The year convention adopted in planting models is that the year of planting is always described as year 0, the year before planting as year − 1, 3 years after planting as year 3 and so on.
2. Effective weed control is essential for success. In the late summer before planting the ground should be treated with glyphosate to kill all persistent weeds. Shortly before planting there should be a treatment with paraquat.
3. In addition to the chemical treatment the ground should be complete ploughed using a normal agricultural plough.
4. For the purposes of this example it has been assumed that this 4 ha wood has a perimeter of 1500 metres. At £217 per 100 metre (rabbit fencing) run this implies a cost of (15 × £217/4ha) = £814 per hectare.
5. In Northern Ireland lime is applied at the rate of 5 to 10 tonnes per hectare to bring the pH up to 6.5. The cost is estimated to be about £45 per hectare.
6. Optimal spacing will vary with the length of the cutting cycle and species chosen. For long coppice cycles of 6 to 8 years, producing larger sized end products, wider spacings (1.5 metres to 3 metres) optimise production in terms of tonnes of dry weight per hectare; while for short rotations of 2 to 4 years close spacings (0.5 metre to 1.0 metre) are more appropriate. Cuttings, 25 centimetres long, are prepared from well ripened wood taken from one-year-old shoots and inserted for two-thirds of their length, in the period February to April. Particularly where cuttings have been cold-stored it is necessary to soak them in water for 36 hours prior to planting.
7. In the winter following planting some of the area may require treatment with propyzamide applied with a 'pepperpot' applicator. From this stage about 10% weed coverage can be tolerated.
8. Cutting back is the process of cutting the shoots close to ground level to encourage coppice growth. This would be done with a clearing saw.

Table D.7 Cash flow for christmas tree operations

All costs are negative and incomes positive.

Costs/incomes are per hectare

Year	Operation/cost/income	Description	Cash flow £ Optimistic forecast	Cash flow £ Pessimistic forecast
0	Ground preparation	Chemical weed – glyphosate	−40	−75
	Fencing		−480	−600
	Plants	£65,000 {Good – 8.0 thousand plants 1.1 m apart	−520	−800
	Planting	£40,000 {Poor – 12.3 thousand plants 0.9 m apart	−320	−490
			−1,360	−1,965
1	Beating up	{Good – 10%	−32	−400
	Plants for beating up	{Poor – 50%	−50	−245
	Weeding	Chemical – propyzamide or simazine	−35	−60
			− 117	− 705
2	Weeding	Chemical – propyzamide or simazine	−35	−60
			−35	−60
3	Weeding	Chemical – glyphosate	−40	−75
			−40	−75
4	Sheering	Good – 80% of trees, poor – 20%	−320	−123
			−320	−123
5	Harvesting cost	{Good – 1.6 thousand trees}	−800	−600
	Income [1]	{Poor – 1.2 thousand trees}	+3,000	+2,152
			+2,200	+1,552
6	Harvesting cost	{Good – 2.4 thousand trees}	−1,200	−900
	Income [1]	{Poor – 1.8 thousand trees}	+6,000	+4,612
			+4,800	+3,712
7	Harvesting cost	{Good – 2.4 thousand trees}	−1,200	−900
	Income [1]	{Poor – 1.8 thousand trees}	+7,200	+5,535
	Destruction of unsaleable trees		−500	−1,500
	Reinstatement costs		−300	−300
			+5,200	+2,835

1. See Section 8.1 Table 8.6 which provides a summary of the range of incomes likely.

125

APPENDIX E
Records – Required for Effective Woodland Management

The value of keeping adequate records has long been recognised in woodland management. As in any other long-term enterprise, a number of different individuals may be involved in the management of a woodland and basic records will therefore provide a continuity that might otherwise be lost.

Only a small number of records may be regarded as essential for effective management throughout the life of a crop. These are:

1. An annotated map, normally at a scale of 1:2500 or 1:10 000 to show:
   – external boundaries of the woodland;
   access routes;
   – location of wayleaves (e.g. cables, water pipes);
   – species boundaries at time of planting.
2. A record of plant origin (including the original seed source if available). Such information will be essential if seed is ever to be collected commercially from the mature crop.
3. The year of planting and original plant spacing (which may be expressed as plants/hectare). These details will be important in assessing the yield of the species at a later date (using published management tables).
4. Dates of grant payment (where applicable).
5. Approved felling licences (where applicable).

A number of the details outlined above will be required for an initial application for approval for a grant aided planting scheme. As well as these records, additional information on work carried out in the wood is likely to be of interest to future managers.

This would include:

- a statement of the objectives of planting (timber production, game management, landscape, conservation, recreation);
- work involved in establishment (e.g. beating up, weeding);
- measures taken to improve site (e.g. drainage, fertiliser application);
- measures taken to protect the crop (e.g. fencing);
- dates of thinning with details of volume removed, markets supplied and income received.

APPENDIX F
Specimen Contract for the Sale of Felled or Standing Timber

(Disclaimer: This specimen contract is provided with the best intentions but no liability will be accepted.)

AGREEMENT NO ....

MEMORANDUM OF AGREEMENT FOR SALE OF STANDING TREES

SELLER 1. ....

(address) ....
(hereinafter called 'the Seller') agrees to sell and

PURCHASER 2. ....

(address) ....
(hereinafter called 'the Purchaser') agrees to purchase, fell and remove

3. (i) Those trees described below and marked for thinning which are standing on the area(s) shown in red on the accompanying map

OR

(ii) Those trees described below being all the trees standing on the area(s) shown in red on the accompanying map.

Species	Number of trees* OR Approximate weights*
....	....
....	....
....	....
....	....

(Approximate weights where shown are not guaranteed by the Seller but are purely for the guidance of the Purchaser.)

*DELETE AS APPROPRIATE

at the price and on the terms and conditions stated below

DURATION OF AGREEMENT

4. Time is of the essence of the Agreement.

The operative date of the Agreement shall be . . . .

and the date for completion of all work shall be . . . .

LOCATION

5. ESTATE . . . .

COUNTY . . . .

PROPERTY AND RISK

6. The risk in all the trees described in Clause 3 shall pass to the Purchaser for the duration of the agreement. The property in those trees which the Seller has agreed to sell shall pass to the Purchaser when the trees have been paid for and cleared.

CONVEYANCE NOTES

7. The Seller may require, by giving notice in writing, that each load uplifted will be accompanied by a conveyance note obtained from the Seller.

FIXED SUM PAYMENT

8. The purchase price shall be £ . . . . plus VAT.

Payment shall be made before the Purchaser starts the clearing of any trees and shall be made in full within 14 days of the date of the Agreement.

------------------------------ OR ------------------------------

Payment shall be made by . . . . instalments as follows

A first instalment of £ . . . . plus VAT to be paid not later than

. . . . and before Purchaser clears any trees. Subsequent

instalments each of £ . . . . plus VAT to be paid not later than the following

dates. . . . .

. . . .

The first instalment shall be deemed to be payment for . . . . of the

number of trees in the Agreement (each subsequent instalment shall be deemed

to be payment for . . . . of the number of the trees in this Agreement).

If at any time the Purchaser has cleared all the trees which he has paid for, he may if he wishes pay the next instalment before the due date and shall then be entitled to clear, remove or cut up the relevant number of trees.

DELETE ONE ALTERNATIVE

DELETE THIS CLAUSE IF NOT APPLICABLE

PAYMENT BY WEIGHT	8. The purchase price shall be £. . . . . per tonne + VAT on weights determined as described in Clause 41.

An initial payment of £. . . . . shall be lodged with the Seller by the Purchaser within 7 days of the adoption of this Agreement. The said initial payment shall be deductable from the final invoice payable on this Agreement. The provisions and requirements of this clause may be waived at the option of the Seller.

DELETE THIS CLAUSE IF NOT APPLICABLE

PAYMENT BY HARVESTED MEASURE

8. The purchase price shall be £ . . . . per cubic metre cleared + VAT.

The volume of each harvested tree will be determined as described in Clause 42.

The harvested trees will be paid for before they are removed from the site by the Purchaser.

-------------------------- OR --------------------------

An initial payment of £ . . . . shall be lodged with the Seller by the Purchaser within 7 days of the adoption of the Agreement. The said initial payment shall be deductable from the final invoice payable on this Agreement

DELETE ONE ALTERNATIVE

DELETE THIS CLAUSE IF NOT APPLICABLE

PAYMENT BY STACKED MEASURE

8. The purchase price shall be £ . . . . per stacked cubic metre + VAT.

The stacked volume will be determined as described in Clause 43.

The stacked material will be paid for before it is removed from the site by the Purchaser.

-------------------------- OR --------------------------

An initial payment of £. . . . . shall be lodged with the Seller by the Purchaser within 7 days of the adoption of this Agreement. The said initial payment shall be deductable from the final invoice payable on this Agreement.

DELETE ONE ALTERNATIVE

DELETE THIS CLAUSE IF NOT APPLICABLE

PAYMENT BY THE PIECE

8. The purchase price will be

£ . . . . per piece + VAT

£ . . . . per piece + VAT

129

The material will be paid for before it is removed from the site by the Purchaser.

-------------------------------- OR ----------------------------------

An initial payment of £ . . . . shall be lodged by the Seller within 7 days of the adoption of this Agreement. The said initial payment shall be deductable from the final invoice payable on the Agreement.

INVOICES

9. When payment is to be made after collection, invoices showing the amount removed will be sent by the Seller as soon as possible after removal. Each invoice shall be paid by the Purchaser not later than the end of the month following the date of the invoice.

RECORD OF CONDI-
TION OF BUILDINGS,
FENCES, ETC

10. An agreed record of the general condition of buildings, walls, gates, fences, hedges, watercourses, roads, rides and tracks at the commencement of this Agreement is as follows:

ENTER DESCRIPTION OF BUILDINGS, FENCES, ETC

METHOD OF
WORKING

11. All trees harvested under the Agreement shall be severed close to ground level and the Purchaser shall carry out the work of harvesting in an orderly and workmanlike manner and as work proceeds shall dispose of brushwood and lop and top to the satisfaction of the Seller and shall stack the produce as directed by the Seller. He shall take all reasonable precautions against damage to the remaining trees on the area or in any neighbouring woods or plantations or to buildings, walls, gates, fences, hedges, drains, watercourses, roads, rides and tracks and shall be liable for any damage thereto due to any act or default of the Purchaser, and shall make good any such damage.

RIGHTS OF ACCESS

12. Rights of access using vehicles within the weight limits shown for the purpose of carrying out the Agreement over the roads shown on the map attached hereto shall be given by the Seller to the Purchaser immediately the purchase price, or, where this is payable by instalments, the first instalment thereof, has been paid. No warranty is given that any other road is suitable for use by vehicles.

USE OF ACCESS
ROADS

13. All vehicles using authorised access routes shall be driven or used with all proper care and at such speed as shall be reasonable having regard to the nature of the route and vehicular load, and to the prevailing weather and road conditions. The Purchaser shall take every reasonable precaution to prevent any damage to the access routes (e.g. by not using them after exceptionally heavy rains or during and after a thaw, until they are suitable for use without causing avoidable damage), and shall, on request, stop the use of any machine or method of working which in the opinion of the Seller is causing, or is likely to cause, damage to standing trees or to any other property and he shall be liable for any wilful or unnecessary damage due to any act or default of the Purchaser, and shall make the same good within one week of its occurrence. The Purchaser must ensure that roads are kept unobstructed at all times and that drains are not blocked as a result of his operations.

SELLER MAY MAKE GOOD DAMAGE	14. In the event of the Purchaser failing to make good the damage or to dispose of the brushwood and lop and top, then the Seller retains the right, 2 weeks after giving written notice to the Purchaser, or after such shorter time as may be reasonable if the proposed work is urgently needed, to arrange for the work to be done. In this event the cost shall be a debt due from the Purchaser and shall be recoverable accordingly.
ORDER OF FELLING	15. The Seller after consultation with the Purchaser shall decide the order in which the timber is to be worked. The order of harvesting and removal shall be mutually agreed before work begins.
HEALTH AND SAFETY AT WORK	16. The Purchaser will accept the responsibility for complying with the provisions of the Health and Safety at Work Act 1974 and all other relevant Acts and regulations in respect of the work comprised in the Agreement and taking place within or upon the land, access routes and other premises of the Seller. The Purchaser will adopt the safety standards relevant to forestry operations as defined and promulgated by the Forestry Safety Council and where, in the estimation of the Seller, there is a serious breach of the safety standards (thereby creating an immediate risk of personal injury) the Seller reserves the right to order the immediate suspension of further work under the agreement until remedial action has been taken by the Purchaser. Any such suspensions shall be without prejudice to any other rights or remedies open to the Seller under the Agreement or otherwise.
ELECTRICITY POWERLINES	17. The Seller will be responsible for laying down the procedure to be followed when the Purchaser is working in the vicinity of any overhead lines, buried cables, pipes or other such obstructions in the area covered by this Agreement, and the location of any such feature will be indicated on the map attached.
PEELING OF PINE TREES	18. During the pine shoot beetle breeding season, from May to September inclusive, any pine trees harvested under the Agreement shall be removed from the Seller's land by the Purchaser within 6 weeks.
TREATMENT OF STUMPS	19. The Purchaser shall treat with Urea or other agreed substance the stump of each conifer tree which he cuts, immediately after and in any case within 30 minutes of the cutting.
FIRES	20. The Purchaser shall not light fires on the Seller's land without the permission of the Seller and shall take all reasonable and proper precautions under the direction of the Seller to prevent and to deal with the risk of fire in the said area or adjoining ground and the Purchaser shall be responsible for any loss whatsoever through fire attributable to his negligence.
POWER SAWS	21. the Seller reserves the right to prohibit the use of power saws or any other machines on his property on a Sunday where their use would, in the Seller's opinion, contribute a nuisance to the general public or to local residents. Such prohibitions shall not be regarded as justifying further charges in the terms, conditions, or prices in the Agreement.
ANIMALS	22. No animals, except those employed to remove trees and produce shall be taken or allowed on the Seller's lands by the Purchaser.
CARAVANS	23. No caravans shall be bought on to the Seller's land without the written consent of the Seller.
FELLING OF TREES NOT INCLUDED IN THE SALE	24. The Purchaser shall not cut down or damage any tree not included in this sale but should any such tree (being a tree not intended to be sold) be cut down or damaged by the Purchaser then the Purchaser shall pay to the Seller as agreed liquidated damages treble the market value thereof and shall retain the tree.
CONDITION OF ROADS, ETC	25. The condition of buildings, walls, gates, fences, hedges, drains, watercourses, roads, rides and tracks at the beginning of the Agreement as recorded in Clause 10 of this Agreement shall be conclusive in all questions arising from the Agreement unless the Seller subsequently improves any of the said buildings, walls, etc, or builds new ones in .which case a record of such improvements or new works shall be made and mutually agreed and thereafter shall form part of the Agreement.

STACKING AND BUILDING SITES	26. The Seller shall make available to the Purchaser a site or sites mutually agreed for stacking the trees sold and resulting produce. No structures or sawmills shall be brought on to the site without the consent of the Seller, such consent will not be unreasonably refused. No payment of these sites shall be required by the Seller during the currency of the Agreement or of any agreed extension thereof but the Purchaser shall be responsible for all charges and liabilities arising from their use.
WATER	27. Subject to all existing rights and without prejudice thereto the Purchaser may take water free of charge from the area for domestic purposes and for such other purposes connected with the felling, conversion and removal of the trees and produce sold to him as the Seller may agree.
BARK AND SAWDUST	28. Unless otherwise agreed the Purchaser shall at his own expense either remove from the Seller's land all bark and sawdust resulting from the Purchaser's operations or shall scatter it in the felling area clear of all ditches, drains, watercourses, roads, rides and tracks.
LIABILITY	29. The Purchaser will indemnify the Seller against claims for loss, injury or damage occasioned by the act or default of the Purchaser in the execution of this Agreement, and will, if so requested, satisfy the Seller that he is adequately insured.
FORCE MAJEURE	30. In the event of any Government regulation or departmental order coming into operation or of any Act of God, strike, lockout or other occurrence of a serious nature beyond the control of the Seller and the Purchaser taking place affecting their ability to perform their obligations under the Agreement and as a result of which the felling of the trees and/or removal and sale thereof are delayed or suspended, the time limit provided for in Clause 4 shall be extended for a period equivalent in working hours and conditions to the period of delay or suspension thereby caused.
FIRE AND WINDBLOW	31. In the event of serious fire or windblow damage occurring on the area covered by this Agreement the Seller or the Purchaser may terminate the Agreement immediately on giving written notice to the other party, but such termination shall be without prejudice to any rights or obligations of either party which may have arisen during the currency of the Agreement. The Seller will allow the Purchaser a reasonable period after such termination in which to remove any harvested trees laying on the area.
EXTENSION OF TIME	32. If the Purchaser shall require an extension of the time limits laid down in Clause 4 he may give notice in writing to the Seller to this effect not less than 4 weeks before expiry of the Agreement setting out his reasons for such request. The Seller shall have an absolute discretion whether to refuse such request or grant the same on such terms as the Seller shall think fit taking into account any increase in volume of the trees caused by extra growth and any loss due to delayed payment of any purchase money consequent on the grant of any such extension.
SUSPENSION OF WORK	33. If for any reason the parties agree that harvesting shall be temporarily suspended on any area and that the Seller shall make available to the Purchaser as a temporary measure alternative areas for harvesting, then where the Purchaser has paid for the trees on the original area the Seller shall calculate the price for the trees remaining uncut and shall credit this amount to the Purchaser towards the price of trees on the alternative areas. Payment of future instalments of the purchase price due on the original area shall be deferred during the period the harvesting on the original area is suspended.
FELLING AND REMOVAL	34. Subject to clauses numbered 30 and 32 the Purchaser shall complete the harvesting and clearance of all areas in accordance with the terms hereof and shall harvest the whole of the said trees and remove the resulting produce from the Seller's lands and leave the stacking and other sites used by the Purchaser clean and tidy and complete his other obligations to the satisfaction of the Seller within the time prescribed in Clause 4 of this Agreement.
REWARDS	35. The Purchaser shall not offer any reward or emolument whatsoever to any person in the employment of the Seller.

| NOT TO ASSIGN | 36. The Purchaser shall not assign his rights under the Agreement except with the consent of the Seller and upon such terms as the Seller may require. |

NOT TO ASSIGN

36. The Purchaser shall not assign his rights under the Agreement except with the consent of the Seller and upon such terms as the Seller may require.

BREACHES GIVING RIGHT TO TERMINATE FORTHWITH

37. If the Purchaser fails to pay sums due in accordance with Clauses 8 and 9 of this Agreement, or if he commits a breach of Clauses 20 or 35 the Seller shall have the right to terminate the Agreement forthwith on giving written intimation to the Purchaser to this effect and any termination shall be without prejudice to any other rights or remedies open to the Seller under the Agreement or otherwise.

OTHER BREACHES

38. If the Purchaser commits a breach of any of the terms and conditions of the Agreement or standard conditions other than those referred to in Clause 37, the Seller shall have the right by written notice to require the Purchaser to remedy the matter within a reasonable specified time and if the matter complained of is not so remedied, the Seller shall have the right to terminate the Agreement forthwith and any termination shall be without prejudice to any other rights or remedies open to the Seller under the Agreement or otherwise.

ACTION ON TERMINATION

39. Upon termination of the Agreement whether by written notice or expiry of time the following shall apply:

  a. the Purchaser shall immediately cease the harvesting of trees and the removal of timber

  b. the Seller may at his discretion allow the Purchaser a further period in which to remove any timber cut before such termination

  c. immediately upon such termination and the expiry of any further period granted under Clause 39 b any harvested trees and any produce therefrom being in or upon the Seller's lands and the property in which is vested in the Purchaser shall vest in and become the property of the Seller together with any remaining trees which have been paid for

  d. the Seller will be entitled either to retain or resell the said remaining trees and any produce therefrom

  e. providing that any other claims against the Purchaser arising from this Agreement have been settled the Seller shall reimburse to the Purchaser the value of all remaining trees and produce therefrom less all costs and losses directly and naturally resulting in the ordinary course of events from termination

  f. in the event of such costs and losses exceeding the said value the Purchaser shall on demand pay to the Seller the amount by which the costs and losses exceed the value

  g. the value of the said remaining trees and produce therefrom will be agreed by the Seller and Purchaser within 90 days of the termination of this Agreement

  h. if the Purchaser and Seller cannot reach agreement on the value of the said standing trees, felled trees and produce the value will be decided by an arbiter agreed by the two parties or in default of such agreement by the President of the Institute of Chartered Foresters or any arbiter of his choice whose decision shall be final and binding.

  i. the Purchaser and Seller shall each pay half the cost of any arbitration required under this clause.

REMOVAL OF EQUIPMENT ETC FROM THE SITE

40. The Purchaser shall within 6 months of the termination of the Agreement remove any buildings, erections or equipment which he may have placed on the area and for which an agreement to rent the land has not been made with the Seller. Should the Purchaser fail to remove such buildings, erections or equipment within the time specified, the Seller may retain or remove and dispose of them as he thinks fit and the Purchaser shall on demand reimburse the Seller for all costs incurred in their disposal after receiving credit for any value which the Seller may place upon them.

WEIGHING OF WOOD   41. Where payment is by weight each load of wood removed from the sale area shall be weighed over a weighbridge agreed by the Seller and Purchaser. Weighbridge tickets for each load shall be given by the Purchaser to the Seller as soon as possible but in any event not later than 14 days after the day of collection.

FELLED MEASURE   42. Where payment is by felled measure the assessment of volume will follow the method described in Forestry Commission Research Information Note 130.

STACKED MEASURE   43. Where payment is by stacked measure the Purchaser undertakes to stack material in a tidy manner so as to facilitate measurement. The volume of a stack of material will be measured as follows:

Volume of stack (cu m) = average height of stack (metres)

× average width of stack (metres) × average length of stack (metres)

PURCHASER   44. The term 'Purchaser' shall include his employees, his agents, sub-contractors, or assignees or the employees of any of them.

Signed . . . . Purchaser . . . . Date . . . .

Signed . . . . Seller . . . . Date . . . .

APPENDIX G
Discounting Tables, range 1 to 14 per cent

Table G.1 Discounting factors at various rates of interest between 1 and 14 per cent

Year	1%	2%	3%	4%	5%	6%	7%	8%	9%	10%	11%	12%	13%	14%
0	1.0000	1.0000	1.0000	1.0000	1.0000	1.0000	1.0000	1.0000	1.0000	1.0000	1.0000	1.0000	1.0000	1.0000
1	0.9901	0.9804	0.9709	0.9615	0.9524	0.9434	0.9346	0.9259	0.9174	0.9091	0.9009	0.8929	0.8850	0.8772
2	0.9803	0.9612	0.9426	0.9246	0.9070	0.8900	0.8734	0.8573	0.8417	0.8264	0.8116	0.7972	0.7831	0.7695
3	0.9706	0.9423	0.9151	0.8890	0.8638	0.8396	0.8163	0.7938	0.7722	0.7513	0.7312	0.7118	0.6931	0.6750
4	0.9610	0.9238	0.8885	0.8548	0.8227	0.7921	0.7629	0.7350	0.7084	0.6830	0.6587	0.6355	0.6133	0.5921
5	0.9515	0.9057	0.8626	0.8219	0.7835	0.7473	0.7130	0.6806	0.6499	0.6209	0.5935	0.5674	0.5428	0.5194
6	0.9420	0.8880	0.8375	0.7903	0.7462	0.7050	0.6663	0.6302	0.5963	0.5645	0.5346	0.5066	0.4803	0.4556
7	0.9327	0.8706	0.8131	0.7599	0.7107	0.6651	0.6227	0.5835	0.5470	0.5132	0.4817	0.4523	0.4251	0.3996
8	0.9235	0.8535	0.7894	0.7307	0.6768	0.6274	0.5820	0.5403	0.5019	0.4665	0.4339	0.4039	0.3762	0.3506
9	0.9143	0.8368	0.7664	0.7026	0.6446	0.5919	0.5439	0.5002	0.4604	0.4241	0.3909	0.3606	0.3329	0.3075
10	0.9053	0.8203	0.7441	0.6756	0.6139	0.5584	0.5083	0.4632	0.4224	0.3855	0.3522	0.3220	0.2946	0.2697
11	0.8963	0.8043	0.7224	0.6496	0.5847	0.5268	0.4751	0.4289	0.3875	0.3505	0.3173	0.2875	0.2607	0.2366
12	0.8874	0.7885	0.7014	0.6246	0.5568	0.4970	0.4440	0.3971	0.3555	0.3186	0.2858	0.2567	0.2307	0.2076
13	0.8787	0.7730	0.6810	0.6006	0.5303	0.4688	0.4150	0.3677	0.3262	0.2897	0.2575	0.2292	0.2042	0.1821
14	0.8700	0.7579	0.6611	0.5775	0.5051	0.4423	0.3878	0.3405	0.2992	0.2633	0.2320	0.2046	0.1807	0.1597
15	0.8613	0.7430	0.6419	0.5553	0.4810	0.4173	0.3624	0.3152	0.2745	0.2394	0.2090	0.1827	0.1599	0.1401
16	0.8528	0.7284	0.6232	0.5339	0.4581	0.3936	0.3387	0.2919	0.2519	0.2176	0.1883	0.1631	0.1415	0.1229
17	0.8444	0.7142	0.6050	0.5134	0.4363	0.3714	0.3166	0.2703	0.2311	0.1978	0.1696	0.1456	0.1252	0.1078
18	0.8360	0.7002	0.5874	0.4936	0.4155	0.3503	0.2959	0.2502	0.2120	0.1799	0.1528	0.1300	0.1108	0.0946
19	0.8277	0.6864	0.5703	0.4746	0.3957	0.3305	0.2765	0.2317	0.1945	0.1635	0.1377	0.1161	0.0981	0.0829
20	0.8195	0.6730	0.5537	0.4564	0.3769	0.3118	0.2584	0.2145	0.1784	0.1486	0.1240	0.1037	0.0868	0.0728
21	0.8114	0.6598	0.5375	0.4388	0.3589	0.2942	0.2415	0.1987	0.1637	0.1351	0.1117	0.0926	0.0768	0.0638
22	0.8034	0.6468	0.5219	0.4220	0.3418	0.2775	0.2257	0.1839	0.1502	0.1228	0.1007	0.0826	0.0680	0.0560
23	0.7954	0.6342	0.5067	0.4057	0.3256	0.2618	0.2109	0.1703	0.1378	0.1117	0.0907	0.0738	0.0601	0.0491
24	0.7876	0.6217	0.4919	0.3901	0.3101	0.2470	0.1971	0.1577	0.1264	0.1015	0.0817	0.0659	0.0532	0.0431
25	0.7798	0.6095	0.4776	0.3751	0.2953	0.2330	0.1842	0.1460	0.1160	0.0923	0.0736	0.0588	0.0471	0.0378
26	0.7720	0.5976	0.4637	0.3607	0.2812	0.2198	0.1722	0.1352	0.1064	0.0839	0.0663	0.0525	0.0417	0.0331
27	0.7644	0.5859	0.4502	0.3468	0.2678	0.2074	0.1609	0.1252	0.0976	0.0763	0.0597	0.0469	0.0369	0.0291
28	0.7568	0.5744	0.4371	0.3335	0.2551	0.1956	0.1504	0.1159	0.0895	0.0693	0.0538	0.0419	0.0326	0.0255
29	0.7493	0.5631	0.4243	0.3207	0.2429	0.1846	0.1406	0.1073	0.0822	0.0630	0.0485	0.0374	0.0289	0.0224
30	0.7419	0.5521	0.4120	0.3083	0.2314	0.1741	0.1314	0.0994	0.0754	0.0573	0.0437	0.0334	0.0256	0.0196
31	0.7346	0.5412	0.4000	0.2965	0.2204	0.1643	0.1228	0.0920	0.0691	0.0521	0.0394	0.0298	0.0226	0.0172
32	0.7273	0.5306	0.3883	0.2851	0.2099	0.1550	0.1147	0.0852	0.0634	0.0474	0.0355	0.0266	0.0200	0.0151
33	0.7201	0.5202	0.3770	0.2741	0.1999	0.1462	0.1072	0.0789	0.0582	0.0431	0.0319	0.0238	0.0177	0.0132
34	0.7130	0.5100	0.3660	0.2636	0.1904	0.1379	0.1002	0.0730	0.0534	0.0391	0.0288	0.0212	0.0157	0.0116
35	0.7059	0.5000	0.3554	0.2534	0.1813	0.1301	0.0937	0.0676	0.0490	0.0356	0.0259	0.0189	0.0139	0.0102
36	0.6989	0.4902	0.3450	0.2437	0.1727	0.1227	0.0875	0.0626	0.0449	0.0323	0.0234	0.0169	0.0123	0.0089
37	0.6920	0.4806	0.3350	0.2343	0.1644	0.1158	0.0818	0.0580	0.0412	0.0294	0.0210	0.0151	0.0109	0.0078
38	0.6852	0.4712	0.3252	0.2253	0.1566	0.1092	0.0765	0.0537	0.0378	0.0267	0.0190	0.0135	0.0096	0.0069
39	0.6784	0.4619	0.3158	0.2166	0.1491	0.1031	0.0715	0.0497	0.0347	0.0243	0.0171	0.0120	0.0085	0.0060
40	0.6717	0.4529	0.3066	0.2083	0.1420	0.0972	0.0668	0.0460	0.0318	0.0221	0.0154	0.0107	0.0075	0.0053

Year	Rates of interest													
	1%	2%	3%	4%	5%	6%	7%	8%	9%	10%	11%	12%	13%	14%
41	0.6650	0.4440	0.2976	0.2003	0.1353	0.0917	0.0624	0.0426	0.0292	0.0201	0.0139	0.0096	0.0067	0.0046
42	0.6584	0.4353	0.2890	0.1926	0.1288	0.0865	0.0583	0.0395	0.0268	0.0183	0.0125	0.0086	0.0059	0.0041
43	0.6519	0.4268	0.2805	0.1852	0.1227	0.0816	0.0545	0.0365	0.0246	0.0166	0.0112	0.0076	0.0052	0.0036
44	0.6454	0.4184	0.2724	0.1780	0.1169	0.0770	0.0509	0.0338	0.0226	0.0151	0.0101	0.0068	0.0046	0.0031
45	0.6391	0.4102	0.2644	0.1712	0.1113	0.0727	0.0476	0.0313	0.0207	0.0137	0.0091	0.0061	0.0041	0.0027
46	0.6327	0.4022	0.2567	0.1646	0.1060	0.0685	0.0445	0.0290	0.0190	0.0125	0.0082	0.0054	0.0036	0.0024
47	0.6265	0.3943	0.2493	0.1583	0.1009	0.0647	0.0416	0.0269	0.0174	0.0113	0.0074	0.0049	0.0032	0.0021
48	0.6203	0.3865	0.2420	0.1522	0.0961	0.0610	0.0389	0.0249	0.0160	0.0103	0.0067	0.0043	0.0028	0.0019
49	0.6141	0.3790	0.2350	0.1463	0.0916	0.0575	0.0363	0.0230	0.0147	0.0094	0.0060	0.0039	0.0025	0.0016
50	0.6080	0.3715	0.2281	0.1407	0.0872	0.0543	0.0339	0.0213	0.0134	0.0085	0.0054	0.0035	0.0022	0.0014
51	0.6020	0.3642	0.2215	0.1353	0.0831	0.0512	0.0317	0.0197	0.0123	0.0077	0.0049	0.0031	0.0020	0.0013
52	0.5961	0.3571	0.2150	0.1301	0.0791	0.0483	0.0297	0.0183	0.0113	0.0070	0.0044	0.0028	0.0017	0.0011
53	0.5902	0.3501	0.2088	0.1251	0.0753	0.0456	0.0277	0.0169	0.0104	0.0064	0.0040	0.0025	0.0015	0.0010
54	0.5843	0.3432	0.2027	0.1203	0.0717	0.0430	0.0259	0.0157	0.0095	0.0058	0.0036	0.0022	0.0014	0.0008
55	0.5785	0.3365	0.1968	0.1157	0.0683	0.0406	0.0242	0.0145	0.0087	0.0053	0.0032	0.0020	0.0012	0.0007
56	0.5728	0.3299	0.1910	0.1112	0.0651	0.0383	0.0226	0.0134	0.0080	0.0048	0.0029	0.0018	0.0011	0.0007
57	0.5671	0.3234	0.1855	0.1069	0.0620	0.0361	0.0211	0.0124	0.0074	0.0044	0.0026	0.0016	0.0009	0.0006
58	0.5615	0.3171	0.1801	0.1028	0.0590	0.0341	0.0198	0.0115	0.0067	0.0040	0.0024	0.0014	0.0008	0.0005
59	0.5560	0.3109	0.1748	0.0989	0.0562	0.0321	0.0185	0.0107	0.0062	0.0036	0.0021	0.0012	0.0007	0.0004
60	0.5504	0.3048	0.1697	0.0951	0.0535	0.0303	0.0173	0.0099	0.0057	0.0033	0.0019	0.0011	0.0007	0.0004
61	0.5450	0.2988	0.1648	0.0914	0.0510	0.0286	0.0161	0.0091	0.0052	0.0030	0.0017	0.0010	0.0006	0.0003
62	0.5396	0.2929	0.1600	0.0879	0.0486	0.0270	0.0151	0.0085	0.0048	0.0027	0.0015	0.0009	0.0005	0.0003
63	0.5343	0.2872	0.1553	0.0845	0.0462	0.0255	0.0141	0.0078	0.0044	0.0025	0.0014	0.0008	0.0005	0.0003
64	0.5290	0.2816	0.1508	0.0813	0.0440	0.0240	0.0132	0.0073	0.0040	0.0022	0.0013	0.0007	0.0004	0.0002
65	0.5237	0.2761	0.1464	0.0781	0.0419	0.0227	0.0123	0.0067	0.0037	0.0020	0.0011	0.0006	0.0004	0.0002
66	0.5185	0.2706	0.1421	0.0751	0.0399	0.0214	0.0115	0.0062	0.0034	0.0019	0.0010	0.0006	0.0003	0.0002
67	0.5134	0.2653	0.1380	0.0722	0.0380	0.0202	0.0107	0.0058	0.0031	0.0017	0.0009	0.0005	0.0003	0.0002
68	0.5083	0.2601	0.1340	0.0695	0.0362	0.0190	0.0100	0.0053	0.0029	0.0015	0.0008	0.0004	0.0002	0.0001
69	0.5033	0.2550	0.1301	0.0668	0.0345	0.0179	0.0094	0.0049	0.0026	0.0014	0.0007	0.0004	0.0002	0.0001
70	0.4983	0.2500	0.1263	0.0642	0.0329	0.0169	0.0088	0.0046	0.0024	0.0013	0.0007	0.0004	0.0002	0.0001
71	0.4934	0.2451	0.1226	0.0617	0.0313	0.0160	0.0082	0.0042	0.0022	0.0012	0.0006	0.0003	0.0002	0.0001
72	0.4885	0.2403	0.1190	0.0594	0.0298	0.0151	0.0077	0.0039	0.0020	0.0010	0.0005	0.0003	0.0002	0.0001
73	0.4837	0.2356	0.1156	0.0571	0.0284	0.0142	0.0072	0.0036	0.0019	0.0010	0.0005	0.0003	0.0001	0.0001
74	0.4789	0.2310	0.1122	0.0549	0.0270	0.0134	0.0067	0.0034	0.0017	0.0009	0.0004	0.0002	0.0001	0.0001
75	0.4741	0.2265	0.1089	0.0528	0.0258	0.0126	0.0063	0.0031	0.0016	0.0008	0.0004	0.0002	0.0001	0.0001
76	0.4694	0.2220	0.1058	0.0508	0.0245	0.0119	0.0058	0.0029	0.0014	0.0007	0.0004	0.0002	0.0001	0.0000
77	0.4648	0.2177	0.1027	0.0488	0.0234	0.0113	0.0055	0.0027	0.0013	0.0006	0.0003	0.0002	0.0001	0.0000
78	0.4602	0.2134	0.0997	0.0469	0.0222	0.0106	0.0051	0.0025	0.0012	0.0006	0.0003	0.0001	0.0001	0.0000
79	0.4556	0.2092	0.0968	0.0451	0.0212	0.0100	0.0048	0.0023	0.0011	0.0005	0.0003	0.0001	0.0001	0.0000
80	0.4511	0.2051	0.0940	0.0434	0.0202	0.0095	0.0045	0.0021	0.0010	0.0005	0.0002	0.0001	0.0001	0.0000
81	0.4467	0.2011	0.0912	0.0417	0.0192	0.0089	0.0042	0.0020	0.0009	0.0004	0.0002	0.0001	0.0001	0.0000
82	0.4422	0.1971	0.0886	0.0401	0.0183	0.0084	0.0039	0.0018	0.0009	0.0004	0.0002	0.0001	0.0000	0.0000
83	0.4379	0.1933	0.0860	0.0386	0.0174	0.0079	0.0036	0.0017	0.0008	0.0004	0.0002	0.0001	0.0000	0.0000
84	0.4335	0.1895	0.0835	0.0371	0.0166	0.0075	0.0034	0.0016	0.0007	0.0003	0.0002	0.0001	0.0000	0.0000
85	0.4292	0.1858	0.0811	0.0357	0.0158	0.0071	0.0032	0.0014	0.0007	0.0003	0.0001	0.0001	0.0000	0.0000
86	0.4250	0.1821	0.0787	0.0343	0.0151	0.0067	0.0030	0.0013	0.0006	0.0003	0.0001	0.0001	0.0000	0.0000
87	0.4208	0.1786	0.0764	0.0330	0.0143	0.0063	0.0028	0.0012	0.0006	0.0003	0.0001	0.0001	0.0000	0.0000
88	0.4166	0.1751	0.0742	0.0317	0.0137	0.0059	0.0026	0.0011	0.0005	0.0002	0.0001	0.0000	0.0000	0.0000
89	0.4125	0.1716	0.0720	0.0305	0.0130	0.0056	0.0024	0.0011	0.0005	0.0002	0.0001	0.0000	0.0000	0.0000
90	0.4084	0.1683	0.0699	0.0293	0.0124	0.0053	0.0023	0.0010	0.0004	0.0002	0.0001	0.0000	0.0000	0.0000

Year	Rates of interest													
	1%	2%	3%	4%	5%	6%	7%	8%	9%	10%	11%	12%	13%	14%
91	0.4043	0.1650	0.0679	0.0282	0.0118	0.0050	0.0021	0.0009	0.0004	0.0002	0.0001	0.0000	0.0000	0.0000
92	0.4003	0.1617	0.0659	0.0271	0.0112	0.0047	0.0020	0.0008	0.0004	0.0002	0.0001	0.0000	0.0000	0.0000
93	0.3964	0.1586	0.0640	0.0261	0.0107	0.0044	0.0019	0.0008	0.0003	0.0001	0.0001	0.0000	0.0000	0.0000
94	0.3925	0.1554	0.0621	0.0251	0.0102	0.0042	0.0017	0.0007	0.0003	0.0001	0.0001	0.0000	0.0000	0.0000
95	0.3886	0.1524	0.0603	0.0241	0.0097	0.0039	0.0016	0.0007	0.0003	0.0001	0.0000	0.0000	0.0000	0.0000
96	0.3847	0.1494	0.0586	0.0232	0.0092	0.0037	0.0015	0.0006	0.0003	0.0001	0.0000	0.0000	0.0000	0.0000
97	0.3809	0.1465	0.0569	0.0223	0.0088	0.0035	0.0014	0.0006	0.0002	0.0001	0.0000	0.0000	0.0000	0.0000
98	0.3771	0.1436	0.0552	0.0214	0.0084	0.0033	0.0013	0.0005	0.0002	0.0001	0.0000	0.0000	0.0000	0.0000
99	0.3734	0.1408	0.0536	0.0206	0.0080	0.0031	0.0012	0.0005	0.0002	0.0001	0.0000	0.0000	0.0000	0.0000
100	0.3697	0.1380	0.0520	0.0198	0.0076	0.0029	0.0012	0.0005	0.0002	0.0001	0.0000	0.0000	0.0000	0.0000

Table G.2 Annual charge to write off £1 over a number of years at various rates of interest

Year	1%	2%	3%	4%	5%	6%	Rates of interest 7%	8%	9%	10%	11%	12%	13%	14%
1	1.0100	1.0200	1.0300	1.0400	1.0500	1.0600	1.0700	1.0800	1.0900	1.1000	1.1100	1.1200	1.1300	1.1400
2	0.5075	0.5150	0.5226	0.5302	0.5378	0.5454	0.5531	0.5608	0.5685	0.5762	0.5839	0.5917	0.5995	0.6073
3	0.3400	0.3468	0.3535	0.3603	0.3672	0.3741	0.3811	0.3880	0.3951	0.4021	0.4092	0.4163	0.4235	0.4307
4	0.2563	0.2626	0.2690	0.2755	0.2820	0.2886	0.2952	0.3019	0.3087	0.3155	0.3223	0.3292	0.3362	0.3432
5	0.2060	0.2122	0.2184	0.2246	0.2310	0.2374	0.2439	0.2505	0.2571	0.2638	0.2706	0.2774	0.2843	0.2913
6	0.1725	0.1785	0.1846	0.1908	0.1970	0.2034	0.2098	0.2163	0.2229	0.2296	0.2364	0.2432	0.2502	0.2572
7	0.1486	0.1545	0.1605	0.1666	0.1728	0.1791	0.1856	0.1921	0.1987	0.2054	0.2122	0.2191	0.2261	0.2332
8	0.1307	0.1365	0.1425	0.1485	0.1547	0.1610	0.1675	0.1740	0.1807	0.1874	0.1943	0.2013	0.2084	0.2156
9	0.1167	0.1225	0.1284	0.1345	0.1407	0.1470	0.1535	0.1601	0.1668	0.1736	0.1806	0.1877	0.1949	0.2022
10	0.1056	0.1113	0.1172	0.1233	0.1295	0.1359	0.1424	0.1490	0.1558	0.1627	0.1698	0.1770	0.1843	0.1917
11	0.0965	0.1022	0.1081	0.1141	0.1204	0.1268	0.1334	0.1401	0.1469	0.1540	0.1611	0.1684	0.1758	0.1834
12	0.0888	0.0946	0.1005	0.1066	0.1128	0.1193	0.1259	0.1327	0.1397	0.1468	0.1540	0.1614	0.1690	0.1767
13	0.0824	0.0881	0.0940	0.1001	0.1065	0.1130	0.1197	0.1265	0.1336	0.1408	0.1482	0.1557	0.1634	0.1712
14	0.0769	0.0826	0.0885	0.0947	0.1010	0.1076	0.1143	0.1213	0.1284	0.1357	0.1432	0.1509	0.1587	0.1666
15	0.0721	0.0778	0.0838	0.0899	0.0963	0.1030	0.1098	0.1168	0.1241	0.1315	0.1391	0.1468	0.1547	0.1628
16	0.0679	0.0737	0.0796	0.0858	0.0923	0.0990	0.1059	0.1130	0.1203	0.1278	0.1355	0.1434	0.1514	0.1596
17	0.0643	0.0700	0.0760	0.0822	0.0887	0.0954	0.1024	0.1096	0.1170	0.1247	0.1325	0.1405	0.1486	0.1569
18	0.0610	0.0667	0.0727	0.0790	0.0855	0.0924	0.0994	0.1067	0.1142	0.1219	0.1298	0.1379	0.1462	0.1546
19	0.0581	0.0638	0.0698	0.0761	0.0827	0.0896	0.0968	0.1041	0.1117	0.1195	0.1276	0.1358	0.1441	0.1527
20	0.0554	0.0612	0.0672	0.0736	0.0802	0.0872	0.0944	0.1019	0.1095	0.1175	0.1256	0.1339	0.1424	0.1510
21	0.0530	0.0588	0.0649	0.0713	0.0780	0.0850	0.0923	0.0998	0.1076	0.1156	0.1238	0.1322	0.1408	0.1495
22	0.0509	0.0566	0.0627	0.0692	0.0760	0.0830	0.0904	0.0980	0.1059	0.1140	0.1223	0.1308	0.1395	0.1483
23	0.0489	0.0547	0.0608	0.0673	0.0741	0.0813	0.0887	0.0964	0.1044	0.1126	0.1210	0.1296	0.1383	0.1472
24	0.0471	0.0529	0.0590	0.0656	0.0725	0.0797	0.0872	0.0950	0.1030	0.1113	0.1198	0.1285	0.1373	0.1463
25	0.0454	0.0512	0.0574	0.0640	0.0710	0.0782	0.0858	0.0937	0.1018	0.1102	0.1187	0.1275	0.1364	0.1455
26	0.0439	0.0497	0.0559	0.0626	0.0696	0.0769	0.0846	0.0925	0.1007	0.1092	0.1178	0.1267	0.1357	0.1448
27	0.0424	0.0483	0.0546	0.0612	0.0683	0.0757	0.0834	0.0914	0.0997	0.1083	0.1170	0.1259	0.1350	0.1442
28	0.0411	0.0470	0.0533	0.0600	0.0671	0.0746	0.0824	0.0905	0.0989	0.1075	0.1163	0.1252	0.1344	0.1437
29	0.0399	0.0458	0.0521	0.0589	0.0660	0.0736	0.0814	0.0896	0.0981	0.1067	0.1156	0.1247	0.1339	0.1432
30	0.0387	0.0446	0.0510	0.0578	0.0651	0.0726	0.0806	0.0888	0.0973	0.1061	0.1150	0.1241	0.1334	0.1428
31	0.0377	0.0436	0.0500	0.0569	0.0641	0.0718	0.0798	0.0881	0.0967	0.1055	0.1145	0.1237	0.1330	0.1425
32	0.0367	0.0426	0.0490	0.0559	0.0633	0.0710	0.0791	0.0875	0.0961	0.1050	0.1140	0.1233	0.1327	0.1421
33	0.0357	0.0417	0.0482	0.0551	0.0625	0.0703	0.0784	0.0869	0.0956	0.1045	0.1136	0.1229	0.1323	0.1419
34	0.0348	0.0408	0.0473	0.0543	0.0618	0.0696	0.0778	0.0863	0.0951	0.1041	0.1133	0.1226	0.1321	0.1416
35	0.0340	0.0400	0.0465	0.0536	0.0611	0.0690	0.0772	0.0858	0.0946	0.1037	0.1129	0.1223	0.1318	0.1414
36	0.0332	0.0392	0.0458	0.0529	0.0604	0.0684	0.0767	0.0853	0.0942	0.1033	0.1126	0.1221	0.1316	0.1413
37	0.0325	0.0385	0.0451	0.0522	0.0598	0.0679	0.0762	0.0849	0.0939	0.1030	0.1124	0.1218	0.1314	0.1411
38	0.0318	0.0378	0.0445	0.0516	0.0593	0.0674	0.0758	0.0845	0.0935	0.1027	0.1121	0.1216	0.1313	0.1410
39	0.0311	0.0372	0.0438	0.0511	0.0588	0.0669	0.0754	0.0842	0.0932	0.1025	0.1119	0.1215	0.1311	0.1409
40	0.0305	0.0366	0.0433	0.0505	0.0583	0.0665	0.0750	0.0839	0.0930	0.1023	0.1117	0.1213	0.1310	0.1407
41	0.0299	0.0360	0.0427	0.0500	0.0578	0.0661	0.0747	0.0836	0.0927	0.1020	0.1115	0.1212	0.1309	0.1407
42	0.0293	0.0354	0.0422	0.0495	0.0574	0.0657	0.0743	0.0833	0.0925	0.1019	0.1114	0.1210	0.1308	0.1406
43	0.0287	0.0349	0.0417	0.0491	0.0570	0.0653	0.0740	0.0830	0.0923	0.1017	0.1113	0.1209	0.1307	0.1405
44	0.0282	0.0344	0.0412	0.0487	0.0566	0.0650	0.0738	0.0828	0.0921	0.1015	0.1111	0.1208	0.1306	0.1404
45	0.0277	0.0339	0.0408	0.0483	0.0563	0.0647	0.0735	0.0826	0.0919	0.1014	0.1110	0.1207	0.1305	0.1404
46	0.0272	0.0335	0.0404	0.0479	0.0559	0.0644	0.0733	0.0824	0.0917	0.1013	0.1109	0.1207	0.1305	0.1403
47	0.0268	0.0330	0.0400	0.0475	0.0556	0.0641	0.0730	0.0822	0.0916	0.1011	0.1108	0.1206	0.1304	0.1403
48	0.0263	0.0326	0.0396	0.0472	0.0553	0.0639	0.0728	0.0820	0.0915	0.1010	0.1107	0.1205	0.1304	0.1403
49	0.0259	0.0322	0.0392	0.0469	0.0550	0.0637	0.0726	0.0819	0.0913	0.1009	0.1107	0.1205	0.1303	0.1402

Year							Rates of interest							
	1%	2%	3%	4%	5%	6%	7%	8%	9%	10%	11%	12%	13%	14%
50	0.0255	0.0318	0.0389	0.0466	0.0548	0.0634	0.0725	0.0817	0.0912	0.1009	0.1106	0.1204	0.1303	0.1402
60	0.0222	0.0288	0.0361	0.0442	0.0528	0.0619	0.0712	0.0808	0.0905	0.1003	0.1102	0.1201	0.1301	0.1401
70	0.0199	0.0267	0.0343	0.0427	0.0517	0.0610	0.0706	0.0804	0.0902	0.1001	0.1101	0.1200	0.1300	0.1400
80	0.0182	0.0252	0.0331	0.0418	0.0510	0.0606	0.0703	0.0802	0.0901	0.1000	0.1100	0.1200	0.1300	0.1400
90	0.0169	0.0240	0.0323	0.0412	0.0506	0.0603	0.0702	0.0801	0.0900	0.1000	0.1100	0.1200	0.1300	0.1400
100	0.0159	0.0232	0.0316	0.0408	0.0504	0.0602	0.0701	0.0800	0.0900	0.1000	0.1100	0.1200	0.1300	0.1400

INDEX

herbicides, 24–26, 29–31, 35–38, 41–43, 58, 120–125
holidays, farm, 51
holly, 12, 13
hoppus foot, 77, 112
hornbeam, 18
hurdles, 11, 75

inheritance tax, 93
inspection, 45
insurance, 25, 26, 27, 38, 49, 51–52, 119
investment appraisal, 83–84

joinery, 12, 72, 73

laburnum, 12
landscape, 10, 12, 57–58, 91, 117
lanes, green, 97
larch, 10, 19, 65, 72
   boatskin quality, 72, 73
   hybrid, 11
   Japanese, 64
lime (tree), 10, 18, 66
liming, 123–124

maintenance, 25, 26, 38, 119–125
management
   expenses, 26, 27, 51, 119
   of game, 10, 11, 46–48, 50, 118
maple, Norway, 18
marketing, 71–77
Mean Annual Increment, 63, 112
measurement, timber, 77, 133–134
mining, use of timber in, 72, 73
mixed woodland, 10, 47, 59, 65
motor-cycling, 51
mound planting, mounding, 24, 29, 112
mulching, 41, 43, 112

Net Present Value, 83, 84, 112
Nothofagus, 18

oak, 9, 10, 18, 59, 63, 65, 66, 67, 72, 75, 89

packaging, 12, 72, 73
pallets, 72, 73, 74
particle board, 72, 73
pesticides, 41
pine, 63, 131
   Corsican, 10, 11, 13, 19
   lodgepole, 13, 19, 75
   Scots, 13, 19, 72, 75
planning permission, 51, 102–103
planting, 24, 26, 33, 53, 71, 73, 107, 119–125
   amenity, 92, 94
planting model, 23, 26–27, 119–125
ploughing, 24, 28, 32, 41, 53, 121, 123, 124
poles, 72, 73, 75, 77
pollarding, 95
ponds, 58, 98
pony-trekking, 51
poplar, 11, 12, 13, 18, 63, 65, 66, 74, 120, 121
   black hybrid, 12

preparation, ground, 24, 25, 26, 28–31, 53, 119–125
prices, 71–78
pruning, 9, 11, 12, 25, 26, 27, 38, 53, 107, 112, 119, 120, 121
pulpwood, 11, 12, 66, 71, 72, 73, 74, 75, 77, 112

rabbits, 13, 50, 122
railway sleepers, 72
record-keeping, 92, 126
recreation, 50–51, 117
regulations, 101–103
rhododendron, 31, 41, 42
riding, 51
ripping, 24, 28
road construction, 24, 25, 26, 31–32, 43–45, 102–103, 119, 123
rotation, 9, 63, 66

safety, 45, 46, 51, 76, 77, 107–108, 131
sawlogs, 71, 72, 73, 112
scarifying, screefing, 24, 29, 53, 112
scrub, 59
seasonal requirements, 52–53
Set-Aside Scheme, *see* grants
shelterbelts, 92, 95, 97
shooting (*see also* deer stalking, game management)
   clay pigeon, 51
shop, farm 74, 90
singling, 9, 113
sleepers, railway, 72
soil types, 17–19, 23, 63
spacing, 9, 10, 12, 59, 63–64
spars, thatching, 11, 75
species choice, 17–19, 23
specifications, market, 77
sports goods, 71, 72
spruce, 63, 102
   Norway, 10, 13, 19, 75
   Sitka, 10, 19
squirrels, 10, 50
stakes, 65, 73, 74, 75, 76
stalking, deer, 48–50
standards, 11, 113
stemwood, 63, 66
surgery, tree, 46, 95
survival games, 51
sycamore, 9, 10, 11, 18, 25, 63, 64, 65, 66, 72, 75

tax, 92–93
thatching spars, 11, 75
thinning, 9, 53, 63, 65–66, 113
track construction, *see* road construction
trails, farm, 51
training, 107–108
treeshelters, 32, 41, 57, 113, 120, 121, 122
turnery, wood, 11, 72, 73, 75

value added tax, 93
vats, 72

Printed in the United Kingdom for Her Majesty's Stationery Office
Dd290516 C60 9/88 3936 12521